Revision Questions for National 5 Chemistry

D A Buchanan

**(Moray House School of Education,
University of Edinburgh)**

J R Melrose

(formerly Lenzie Academy)

Published by
Chemcord
Inch Keith
East Kilbride
Glasgow

ISBN 9781870570923

Printed by Bell and Bain Ltd, Glasgow

Index

Note to teachers / students

* The questions are specifically written to test students' understanding
    - of the key ideas in the National 5 Chemistry course,
    - of the key ideas in the National 4 Chemistry course that are judged to be helpful for progression to National 5.

    A small number of questions are also included to cover the content of the National 4 course for which there is no obvious progression to National 5. These are marked with a *.

* The aim is to give students practice in the kinds of question used in the National 5 examination and other course assessments.

* The questions have also been found to be an invaluable revision aid.

* The questions cover both Knowledge and understanding and Problem solving.

* The exercises are, by and large, independent of each other and consequently they can be used to fit almost any teaching order. Hey can be used in a variety of situations, e.g. for examination revision, self-study time in school, homework, etc.

* Some questions refer to the Data Booklet. This can be downloaded from the SQA website.

    (www.sqa.org.uk/files_ccc/ChemistryDataBookletSQPN5.pdf).

* A complete set of answers is available in the publication *"Answers to Revision Questions for National 5 Chemistry"*. Answers are structured with sufficient detail to assist the student in their understanding of the related content.

Acknowledgement

A number of questions in the exercises come from or have evolved from questions used in Scottish Qualifications Authority (SQA) examinations. The publisher wishes to thank the SQA for permission to use the examination questions in this way.

Rate of reactions

1. Different chemical reactions happen at different speeds.
   (a) Give an example of a reaction in the lab that
       (i) is almost instantaneous,
       (ii) takes a few minutes to finish.
   (b) List the following in order of rate of reaction, fastest first:
       milk turning sour,   *an egg frying,*
       a motor car rusting,   *a match igniting*

2. The rate of a reaction depends on the reaction conditions.
   Explain the way in which each of the following affects the speed of a reaction.
   (a) particle size of the reactants
   (b) concentration of the reactants
   (c) temperature of the reactants

3. Natural gas burns in a bunsen burner.
   (a) What happens to the temperature of the flame when the air hole is opened.
   (b) Explain your answer.

4. A jet of petrol is sprayed into the cylinders of a car engine.
   Explain why the spray of petrol burns faster than the petrol in the bowl.

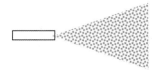

petrol spray   **petrol in a bowl**

5. Explain each of the following.
   (a) Small sticks of wood burn faster than logs.
   (b) When air is blown on to a fire, the fire burns brighter.
   (c) Food is preserved longer when stored in a fridge.
   (d) Plants grow faster in a green-house than in the open-air.
   (e) Large potatoes take longer to cook than small potatoes.
   (f) An oxy-acetylene flame is hot enough to cut through metal.
       The flame obtained by burning acetylene in air is not.

6. Three experiments are set up as shown. Each experiment is carried out at room temperature and the mass of magnesium is the same in each case.

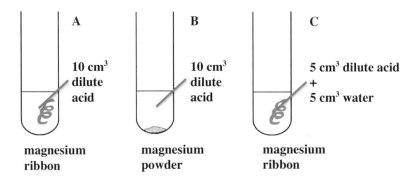

	A	B	C
	10 cm³ dilute acid	10 cm³ dilute acid	5 cm³ dilute acid + 5 cm³ water
	magnesium ribbon	magnesium powder	magnesium ribbon

   (a) Explain any difference that would be observed between
       (i) **A** and **B**,
       (ii) **A** and **C**.
   (b) Explain any difference that would be observed if experiment **A** was repeated at 50 °C.

7. A student set up the three experiments shown.

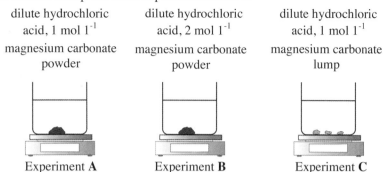

| dilute hydrochloric acid, 1 mol l⁻¹ magnesium carbonate powder | dilute hydrochloric acid, 2 mol l⁻¹ magnesium carbonate powder | dilute hydrochloric acid, 1 mol l⁻¹ magnesium carbonate lump |

$$\text{dilute hydrochloric acid, } 1 \text{ mol } l^{-1}$$
$$\text{magnesium carbonate powder}$$

$$\text{dilute hydrochloric acid, } 2 \text{ mol } l^{-1}$$
$$\text{magnesium carbonate powder}$$

$$\text{dilute hydrochloric acid, } 1 \text{ mol } l^{-1}$$
$$\text{magnesium carbonate lump}$$

Experiment **A**   Experiment **B**   Experiment **C**

In each experiment, some magnesium carbonate remained unreacted.

(a) Place the experiments in order of increasing reaction rate.

(b) At the end of all the experiments, the readings showed a decrease in mass.

Why was the decrease in mass twice as much in Experiment **B** as in Experiment **A**?

8. A company produced sweets in the form of a powder that fizzed in water. Three different experiments were carried out to check the fizziness of the sweets .

Experiment	Mass of powder added to 1 litre of water / g	Temperature / °C
1	40	25
2	40	37
3	20	25

For each experiment, a graph was plotted of the volume of gas produced against time.

The graph for Experiment 1 is shown.

Volume of gas

Experiment 1

Time

Copy the graph and draw curves to represent Experiment 2 and Experiment 3.

9. The graph shows the volume of carbon dioxide produced in a reaction of calcium carbonate powder with dilute hydrochloric acid.

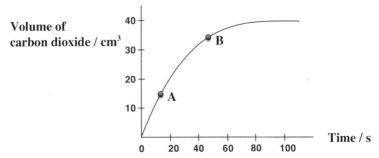

(a) (i) Is the rate of reaction faster at **A** or **B**?

(ii) Give a reason for your answer.

The experiment was repeated under two different conditions. For both reactions, the volume and concentration of the hydrochloric acid remained the same.

(b) (i) What would have happened to the volume of gas produced in the first 20 s when the temperature was increased?

(ii) What would have been the final volume of gas produced when the same mass of calcium carbonate lumps was used?

10. The graph shows the volume of hydrogen produced in the reaction of zinc powder and zinc granules with excess dilute sulphuric acid.

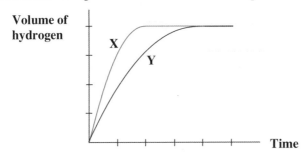

(a) (i) Which curve, **X** or **Y**, shows the results using zinc powder?
(ii) Explain your answer.

(b) State **three** variables that must be kept the same when comparing the rates of the reactions.

11. The graph shows the volume of gas produced in the reaction of marble
     chips with excess dilute sulphuric acid in two experiments.

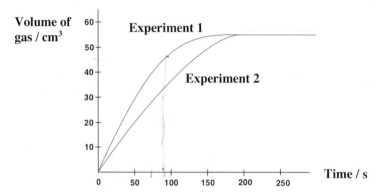

(a) What volume of gas was produced in Experiment 1 during the first 90 s?

(b) In the initial stages, the reaction in Experiment 2 was slower than in
     Experiment 1.

     (i)   How can this be concluded from the graph?

     (ii) Suggest **two** changes in conditions that could have resulted in the
           slower reaction.

(c) The same mass of marble chips was used in each experiment.
     How can this be concluded from the graph?

12. The graph shows the volume of hydrogen produced in the reaction of 10 g of magnesium powder with excess 1 mol l^{-1} hydrochloric acid.

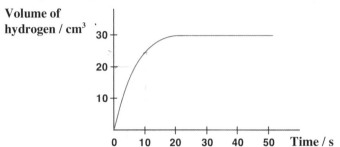

(a) State the volume of hydrogen that was produced after 10 s.

(b) State the time required to produce 20 cm^3 of hydrogen.

(c) State the total volume of hydrogen produced.

(d) Copy the graph and add a curve to show the results that you would expect to obtain
   (i) if the same mass of magnesium powder was added to excess of 2 mol l^{-1} hydrochloric acid (label **X**),
   (ii) if the same mass of magnesium ribbon was added to excess of 1 mol l^{-1} hydrochloric acid (label **Y**),
   (iii) if 5 g of magnesium powder was added to excess of 1 mol l^{-1} hydrochloric acid (label **Z**).

Average rate of reaction

1. In a chemical reaction, 150 cm^3 of gas is produced in 20 s.

    Calculate the average rate of reaction over this period of time.

2. In a chemical reaction, the change in mass of the reactants is 0.36 g in 40 minutes.

    Calculate the average rate of reaction over this period of time.

3. The table shows how the volume of gas produced varies with time in a chemical reaction.

Time /s	Volume of gas / cm^3
0	0
10	28
20	40
30	50
40	56
50	59
60	61

    Calculate the average rate of reaction over the period

    (a)   0 s to 20 s,

    (b)   20 s to 40 s,

    (c)   40 s to 60 s.

4. The table shows how the total mass of reactants varies with time in a chemical reaction.

Time /min	Mass of reactants /g
0	246.24
2	245.98
4	245.82
6	245.72
8	245.64
10	245.64
12	245.51

Calculate the average rate of reaction over the period

(a) 0 to 6 min,

(b) 6 to 12 min.

5. The graph shows how the volume of gas produced varies with time in a chemical reaction.

Volume of gas produced / cm³

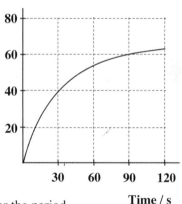

Time / s

Calculate the average rate of reaction over the period

(a) 0 to 30 s,

(b) 30 s to 60 s.

Chemical Changes and Structure

6. The graph shows how the mass of reactants changes with time in a chemical reaction.

 Mass of reactants / g

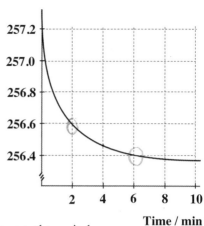

Time / min

Calculate the average rate of reaction over the period

(a) 0 to 2 minutes,

(b) 2 to 6 minutes.

Catalysts

1. (a) What is meant by a catalyst?
    (b) (i)   Does a catalyst take part in a reaction?
         (ii) Is the catalyst chemically changed in the reaction?
         (iii) Can the catalyst be recovered at the end of the reaction?

2. (a) What is meant by an enzyme?
    (b) Give an example of the use of an enzyme in everyday life.

3. Catalytic converters are fitted to the exhaust systems of cars.

harmless gases

ceramic material covered with catalyst

harmful gases ↗

    (a) Why do manufacturers fit a catalytic converter to car exhaust systems?
    (b) Suggest why the catalyst is spread over a large surface area.

4. Reactions take place on the surface of a catalyst.
    A catalyst can be produced in pellets of different shapes.

| A | B | C | D |

    Explain which of the shapes **A**, **B**, **C** or **D** would be best for use as a catalyst.

5. Catalysts are used in many industrial reactions.

    (a) Explain why catalysts are used in many industrial reactions.

    (b) In the chemical industry, give an example of the use of a catalyst.

6. Hydrogen peroxide solution decomposes to produce oxygen. The graph shows the volume of oxygen produced with time in one experiment.

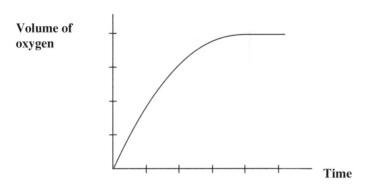

The experiment was repeated with the only change being the addition of 1 g of manganese dioxide, a catalyst for the reaction.

    (a) What mass of manganese dioxide will be left at the end of the second experiment?

    (b) Copy the graph and add a second curve to show the results that you would expect in the second experiment (label **X**).

Elements and compounds

1. (a) Approximately how many elements are listed in the Periodic Table?
   (b) Name **two** naturally occurring elements that are
      (i)   metallic,
      (ii) non-metallic.
   (c) Name **two** elements that are
      (i)   solid at room temperature,
      (ii) liquid at room temperature,
      (iii) gas at room temperature,
      (iv) made by scientists.

2. Find the name and symbol for an element that is
   (a) stored under oil,
   (b) stored under water,
   (c) used as 'lead' in pencils,
   (d) once used to fill airships
   (e) used as the metal in domestic lightbulbs,
   (f) used as the gas in domestic lightbulbs,
   (g) used to kill germs in swimming baths,
   (h) now used in lighter than air balloons,
   (i) called after a planet,
   (j) called after Dimitri Mendeleev,
   (k) called after an American state,
   (l) called after Albert Einstein,
   (m) called after a continent,
   (n) called after a village in Scotland,
   (o) called after the man who discovered dynamite,
   (p) called after the woman who discovered radium.

3. The elements are arranged in the Periodic Table.
   Explain what is meant by
   (a) a group,
   (b) a period.

4. (a) Name the elements with each of the following atomic numbers.
      (i)   23   (ii) 3   (iii) 18   (iv) 28
   (b) Give the atomic number of each of the following elements.
      (i)   chlorine (ii) helium   (iii) uranium   (iv) iron

5. There is a special scale to measure the mass of something as light as an atom.
    (a) (i)   Name this scale.
        (ii) Why does the scale **not** have units?
    (b) Give the mass on this scale for an atom of
        (i)   oxygen   (ii)   carbon
        (iii) sulphur   (iv)   magnesium.

6. Look at the following list of elements:

sodium,	iron,	argon,	chlorine,	magnesium
copper,	bromine,	helium,	potassium,	sulphur,
rubidium,	iodine,	xenon,	nickel,	carbon

    (a) Name the elements that are members of each of the following families.
        (i)   the halogens   (ii)   the alkali metals
        (iii) the transition metals   (iv)   the noble gases
    (b) State a chemical property of
        (i)   the alkali metals,   (ii)   the noble gases.

7. Germanium is so similar to silicon that it was once called "eka silicon".
    Why are germanium and silicon similar to each other?

8. Dimitri Mendeleev used the properties of the elements to help arrange them in his Periodic Table. He left gaps in the table if no known element fitted and then made predictions about the properties of the elements that should occupy these gaps.
    (a) Predict whether astatine (atomic number 85) is likely to be a solid, a liquid or a gas at room temperature.
    (b) Predict a chemical property of caesium (atomic number 55).

9. Some trends in the reactions of elements and their compounds can be shown on the Periodic Table. Here is one example that deals with the extraction of metals.

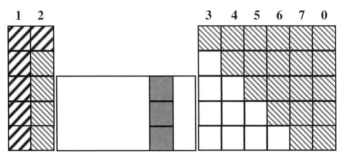

Key

Source of metal	Extraction method
Soluble compounds	Using electricity
Insoluble compounds	Using electricity
Free metals	Not required
Insoluble oxides / sulphides	Heating with carbon or carbon monoxide

(a) Using the above information and a Periodic Table in the Data Booklet, suggest an extraction method for strontium (atomic number 38).

(b) What general statement can be made about the position of a metal in the Periodic Table and its ease of extraction?

10. Refer to page 8 of the Data Booklet. For each of the following two compounds (not shown in the Data Booklet), predict the letter(s) that would be used in the table to indicate its solubility. Choose from vs – very soluble, s – soluble or i – insoluble.

(a) rubidium chloride

(b) radium sulphate

11. Certain chemicals used to be added to petrol to prevent 'pinking' in car engines.
Pinking means that the petrol-air mixture explodes too soon.
It is found that iodine compounds are more effective in preventing pinking than bromine or chlorine compounds.
Compounds of selenium (atomic number 34) and tellurium (atomic number 52) are both more effective than iodine compounds, with tellurium compounds better than selenium compounds.
Use this information to explain why the lead compound, tetraethyl lead, was added to some petrols to prevent pinking.

12. The halogens are the elements in Group 7 of the Periodic Table.
Their compounds are known as halides.
A student was investigating the reactions between solutions of certain halogens and halides.

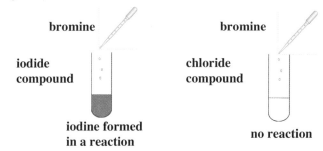

The results of his investigations are summarised in the following table.

		Halide		
		iodide	bromide	chloride
Halogen	chlorine	✓	✓	✗
	bromine	✓	✗	✗
	iodine	✗	✗	✗

✓ = reaction
✗ = no reaction

(a) Use this information to write a general statement about reactions between halogens and halides.
(b) Predict what would happen if chlorine was added to a fluoride.

13. The graph shows the ionisation energy for the first 20 elements.

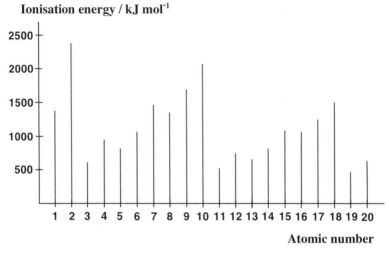

Ionisation energy / kJ mol⁻¹

Atomic number

(a) Describe the general trend in ionisation energy going across the period from lithium to neon.

(b) Describe the trend in ionisation energy going down a group.

14. (a) What is the difference between an element and a compound?

(b) Divide the following list of substances into elements and compounds.
carbon,   petrol,   sodium chloride,   zinc,   oxygen,
sugar,   gold,   copper sulphate,   nitrogen, aluminium,
silver oxide, alcohol

15. (a) Name the compound that is formed when each of the following pairs of elements join up.

(i) magnesium and chlorine

(ii) lead and sulphur

(iii) sodium and oxygen

(iv) hydrogen and iodine

(b) Name **two** possible compounds containing potassium, sulphur and oxygen.

16. Copy the list of substances and complete all the columns.
(One example is already done for you.)

Formula of substance	Element	Compound	Atoms present
$CaSO_4$	✗	✓	calcium, sulphur, oxygen
He			
NaBr			
LiCl			
ZnI_2			
Fe			
KNO_3			
Xe			
I_2			

17. Read the passage below carefully.

> *Oxygen is involved in many everyday reactions.*
>
> *Glucose is a compound containing carbon, hydrogen and oxygen. It is built up in plants from carbon dioxide and water in a process called photosynthesis. Oxygen is released in the reaction.*
>
> *The starch in our food is broken down to form glucose. During respiration, glucose and oxygen react and energy is produced in the process.*
>
> *The reaction of oxygen with methane releases energy that can be used as a source of heat in our houses. In a car engine, petrol combines with oxygen in another energy-producing reaction.*
>
> *Oxygen, as well as water, is involved in the rusting of iron - a reaction that costs this country many millions of pounds each year. The iron can be protected by coating the surface with zinc, copper or gold.*

Make a table to show all the **elements** and **compounds** mentioned in the passage.

Atomic structure

1. (a) (i)   What name is given to the "core" at the centre of the atom?
        (ii) What charge has the 'core'?
        (iii) Name the two subatomic particles found in the 'core'.
    (b) (i)   Name the particles that move around the outside of the atom.
        (ii) What charge do these particles have?
    (c) Explain why an atom is neutral.

2. Copy and complete the following table.

Subatomic particle	Mass	Charge	Location in atom
electron			
proton			
neutron			

3. (a) Name the elements with each of the following electron arrangements.
        (i)   2,8,1   (ii) 2,8   (iii) 2,8,3
        (iv) 2,4   (v) 2,7   (vi) 2,8,4
    (b) Which **two** of the above elements will have similar chemical properties?

4. (a) Which element has atoms with 17 protons in the nucleus?
    (b) Which element has 11 electrons in each of its atoms?
    (c) Which element has atoms with an electron arrangement of 2,6?

5. (a) For an atom of an element, explain what is meant by
        (i) the atomic number,
        (ii) the mass number.
    (b) An atom of potassium can be written as $^x_y K$.
        State the information that is given by **x** and **y**.

6. (a) Copy and complete the following table.

Element	Atomic number	Mass number	Number of protons	Number of neutrons	Number of electrons
Ne		22			
N				7	
Ca		40			
A	4	9			
B		14			6
C		80	36		
D			10	10	
E				17	15

(b) Identify elements **A, B, C, D** and **E**.

7. Calculate the number of protons, neutrons and electrons in each of the following atoms of elements.

(a) $^{23}_{11}Na$ (b) $^{16}_{8}O$ (c) $^{3}_{1}H$

(d) $^{35}_{17}Cl$ (e) $^{1}_{1}H$ (f) $^{40}_{20}Ca$

(g) $^{39}_{19}K$ (h) $^{7}_{3}Li$ (i) $^{32}_{16}S$

8. An atom of sodium can be written as $^{23}_{11}Na$.
Write each of the atoms below in a similar way.
(a) An oxygen atom with 10 neutrons.
(b) An atom, atomic number 6, with 7 neutrons.
(c) An atom with 17 protons and 20 neutrons.
(d) An atom of hydrogen, mass number 3.

9. An alpha particle is a positive particle that can gain two electrons to become a neutral atom.
An alpha particle has a mass number of 4 and an atomic number of 2.

Calculate the number of protons, neutrons and electrons in an alpha particle.

10. Atom **A** has mass number 239 and atomic number 93.
Atom **B** has a mass number 239 and atomic number 94.
   (a) How many protons has **A**?
   (b) How many neutrons has **B**?
   (c) (i) Are atoms **A** and **B** of the same element?
       (ii) Explain your answer.

11. In the reactions occurring in the sun, some atoms collide with such force that their nuclei join together to make one new nucleus.
   (a) Why must a new element be formed in reactions of this kind?
   (b) Helium is formed in solar reactions.
       Nuclei of which element join together to make helium?

12. Normal hydrogen atoms, $_1^1 H$, are known as protium atoms.
   (a) (i) How many protons are there in a protium nucleus?
       (ii) How many neutrons are there in a protium nucleus?
       (iii) What name is given to the total number of protons and neutrons in the nucleus of an atom?
   (b) Deuterium, $_1^2 H$, is another type of hydrogen atom.
       (i) How many protons are there in a deuterium nucleus?
       (ii) How many neutrons are there in a deuterium nucleus?
       (iii) Suggest why deuterium is sometimes referred to as "heavy" hydrogen.
   (c) Tritium is a third type of hydrogen atom with a mass number of 3.
       How many protons and neutrons are there in a tritium nucleus?

Relative atomic mass (atomic weight)

1. Bromine has a relative atomic mass of 80. Analysis of a sample of bromine shows that it contains two isotopes, one with a relative mass of 79 and the other with a relative mass of 81.

   (a) Explain what is meant by isotopes.

   (b) What can be said about the proportions of the isotopes in the sample?

2. $_{10}^{20}$Ne and $_{10}^{22}$Ne are two different kinds of neon atom.

   (a) In what ways are the kinds of neon atom different?

   (b) Explain why the atoms can be regarded as atoms of the same element.

   (c) What further information is needed to calculate the relative atomic mass (atomic weight) of neon?

3. Two types of chlorine atom are $_{17}^{35}$Cl and $_{17}^{37}$Cl.

   Chlorine has a relative atomic mass of 35.5.

   (a) What term is used to describe the different types of chlorine atom?

   (b) What can be said about the proportions of each type of atom in chlorine?

4. Copper has a relative atomic mass (atomic weight) of 63.5. It contains two different kinds of atom: ^{63}Cu and ^{65}Cu.

   (a) How many neutrons are present in each kind of atom?

   (b) Which kind of atom is more common in copper?

5. The graph shows the percentage of the two different isotopes in a sample of lithium.

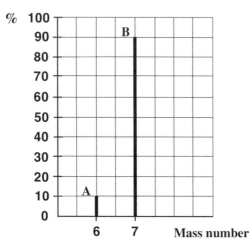

The relative atomic mass of lithium can be calculated using the formula:

$$\frac{(\text{mass of isotope } \mathbf{A} \times \%) + (\text{mass of isotope } \mathbf{B} \times \%)}{100}$$

(a) Explain what is meant by the relative atomic mass of an element.

(b) Using the information in the graph, calculate the relative atomic mass of lithium.

6. Although listed as 12 in the Data Booklet, the relative atomic mass (RAM) of carbon is not actually a whole number.

(a) Why is the RAM of carbon **not** a whole number?

(b) Why is the RAM of carbon listed as a whole number?

Covalent bonding

1. Explain what is meant by
    (a) a molecule,
    (b) a covalent bond.

2. (a) Atoms of what kind of elements form covalent bonds?
    (b) Which of the following are covalent compounds?
(i) sodium chloride	(ii) hydrogen chloride
(iii) carbon sulphide	(iv) aluminium nitrate
(v) iron oxide	(vi) phosphorus oxide
(vii) copper sulphate	(viii) CH_3Cl
(ix) MgO	(x) NO_2
(xi) $FeCl_2$	(xii) C_2H_5OH
(xiii) Na_2CO_3	(xiv) $C_6H_{12}O_6$

3. Write the chemical formula for each of the following substances.

    (a)

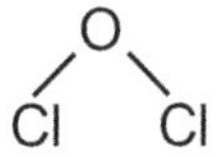

    (b)   H—H

    (c)

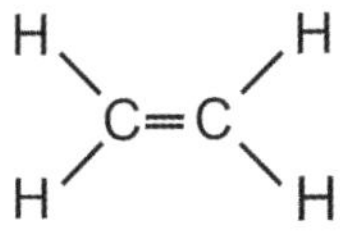

    (d)

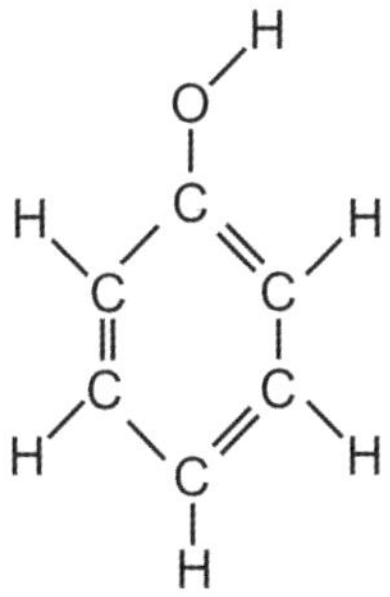

    (e)

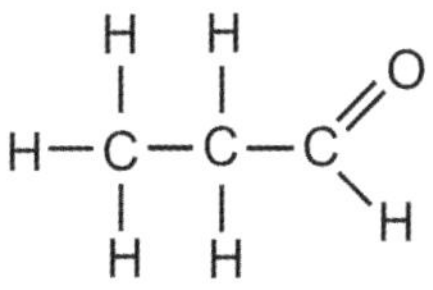

4. The molecules below show the way atoms are arranged in different molecules.

(a)   (b)   (c)

(d)   (e)   (f)

(g)

Choose a name for each substance from the following list:

chlorine,   hydrogen oxide,   carbon chloride,   nitrogen,
oxygen,   hydrogen chloride,   nitrogen hydride

5. Write the chemical formula for each of the following compounds.
   (a) sulphur trioxide   (b) carbon dioxide
   (c) carbon monoxide   (d) silicon tetrafluoride
   (e) phosphorus pentachloride (f) uranium hexafluoride

6. (a) Explain what is meant by a diatomic molecule.
   (b) Which of the following elements exist as diatomic molecules?
       (i)   calcium   (ii)   carbon
       (iii) nitrogen   (iv)   aluminium
       (v)   hydrogen   (vi)   neon
       (vii) chlorine   (viii) sulphur
       (ix)   magnesium   (x)   oxygen
       (xi)   fluorine   (xii)   argon
   (c) Which of the following compounds exist as diatomic molecules?
       (i) CH_2O (ii)   HCl -
       (iii) NH_3 (iv)   CO
       (v) CH_2Cl_2 (vi) SO_2

7. Draw diagrams to show how the outer electrons form covalent bonds in each of the following molecules.
    (a) hydrogen   (b) oxygen
    (c) fluorine   (d) phosphorus chloride
    (e) hydrogen chloride   (f) hydrogen oxide
    (g) carbon fluoride   (h) carbon dioxide
    (i) nitrogen hydride   (j) sulphur fluoride

8. Write the chemical formula for each of the following compounds.
    (a) hydrogen sulphide   (b) phosphorus fluoride
    (c) nitrogen chloride   (d) hydrogen iodide
    (e) sulphur chloride   (f) silicon oxide

9. Explain what is meant by
    (a) the chemical formula for a covalent substance,
    (b) the full structural formula.

10. (a) Make a drawing to show the shape of each of the following molecules.
         (i) N_2 (ii) CCl_4
         (iii) NH_3 (iv) H_2O
    (b) What name can be used to describe the shape of a CCl_4 molecule?
    (c) Why is the molecule of H_2O **not** linear?

11. The atoms in a hydrogen molecule are held together by a covalent bond.
    A covalent bond is a shared pair of electrons.
    Explain how this holds the atoms together.

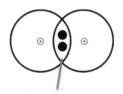

shared pair of electrons

12. Methoxyethane($CH_3OC_2H_5$) and methanol (CH_2O) are both covalent carbon compounds.

Draw the full structural formula for

(a)   methoxyethane,

(b)   methanol.

13. Ethyne is made up of molecules that contain only carbon and hydrogen atoms.
The formula mass for ethyne is 26.

Draw the full structural formula for ethyne.

14.

Gas	Relative atomic mass	Density (relative to hydrogen)
hydrogen	1	1
helium	4	2
nitrogen	14	14
oxygen	16	16
neon	20	10
chlorine	35.5	35.5
argon	40	20

(a)   Some of the gases in the table are made up of diatomic molecules.
What general statement can be made about the relationship between the relative atomic mass and density (relative to hydrogen) for the diatomic molecules?

(b)   If the relative atomic mass of xenon is 131, predict its density (relative to hydrogen).

Ionic bonding

1. Explain what is meant by
   (a) an ion,
   (b) an ionic bond.

2. What is the charge on each of the following ions?
   (a) potassium   (b) sulphur
   (c) nitrogen   (d) bromine
   (e) aluminium   (f) strontium
   (g) fluorine   (h) caesium

3. It is often said that metal atoms 'want' to lose electrons to form positive ions.
   (a) To what extent do you agree with this statement?
   (b) Explain your thinking.

4. What is the difference between the information given by the formula for a covalent compound and the formula for an ionic compound?

5. (a) Explain clearly what happens when
      (i) an atom of chlorine forms a chloride ion,
      (ii) an atom of calcium forms a calcium ion.
   (b) What happens during the formation of an ionic bond in calcium chloride?

6. A compound is formed from a Group 1 clement and a Group 7 element.
   Choose two elements and show by means of a diagram what happens to the electrons in the outer shell (energy level) of the atoms involved.

7. (a) Copy and complete the following table to show the numbers of protons and electrons in each of the following ions.

Ion	Number of protons	Number of electrons
Ca^{2+}		
Cl^-		
Al^{3+}		
O^{2-}		

(b) Look at the information in the table.

Ion	Number of protons	Number of electrons
zinc	30	28
sulphide	16	18
copper	29	28
tin	50	48

Using the information in the table, show how you would represent

(i) the zinc ion,   (ii) the sulphide ion,

(iii) the copper ion,   (iv) the tin ion.

8. Hydrogen chloride is made up of molecules but sodium chloride exists as a lattice.

(a) Explain what is meant by a lattice.

(b) Explain why the word "molecule" has no meaning when we are thinking of sodium chloride.

9. Write the ionic formula and formula (without charges on the ions) for each of the following compounds.

(a) sodium bromide   (b) potassium oxide

(c) magnesium chloride   (d) calcium sulphide

(e) aluminium oxide   (f) magnesium nitride

(g) barium oxide   (h) caesium bromide

10. Write the ionic formula and formula (without charges on the ions) for each of the following compounds.

(a) lead(II) bromide
(b) copper(I) iodide
(c) iron(III) chloride
(d) nickel(II) sulphide
(e) silver(I) oxide
(f) vanadium(V) oxide

11. Write the ionic formula and formula (without charges on the ions) for each of the following compounds.

(a) lithium hydroxide
(b) potassium sulphite
(c) sodium nitrate
(d) iron(II) hydroxide
(e) ammonium chloride
(f) magnesium carbonate
(g) radium chromate
(h) ammonium sulphate
(g) rubidium phosphate
(h) barium hydrogencarbonate
(i) potassium permanganate
(j) aluminium hydrogensulphate

12. Write the ionic formula and formula (without charges on the ions) for each of the following compounds.

(a) sodium iodide
(b) magnesium hydroxide
(c) iron(III) chloride
(d) calcium nitrate
(e) ammonium bromide
(f) rubidium fluoride
(g) magnesium sulphate
(h) ammonium carbonate
(i) copper(II) carbonate
(j) sodium sulphide
(k) radium phosphate
(l) tin(IV) oxide

Properties of substances

1. (a) Draw a labelled diagram to show how elements can be tested to classify them as conductors or non-conductors.
    (b) Which of the following elements conduct electricity?
      (i)   solid iron   (ii)   molten copper
      (iii) liquid oxygen   (iv)   liquid sodium
      (v)   solid sulphur   (vi)   argon gas
      (vii) liquid mercury   (viii) solid magnesium
      (ix)   liquid bromine   (x)   chlorine gas

2. Consider the following four substances.

    sucrose ($C_6H_{12}O_6$),   baking powder ($NaHCO_3$)
    potash (KCl),   acetone (C_2H_6O)

    (a) Name the substances that conduct electricity when in aqueous solution.
    (b) Explain why the substances you have chosen do **not** conduct when solid.

3. Copy and complete the following table using a √ to show a conductor and an ✗ to show a non-conductor.

Substance	In solid	In solution	As a liquid (molten)
Metal element		insoluble	
Covalent substance (element or compound)			
Ionic compound			

4. The electrical conductivities of substances **A**, **B** and **C** were measured and the results are shown. (0 is **no** conduction, + is conducts)

Substance	In solid state	Dissolved in water	In molten state
A	0	+	+
B	+	insoluble	+
C	0	0	0

(a) Which substance could be lead?

(b) Which substance could be potassium bromide?

(c) Which substance could be iodine?

5.

	P	Q	R	S
Solubility in water	soluble	insoluble	soluble	soluble
Colour of solution	colourless		blue	colourless
Electrical conductivity in solid state	does not conduct	conducts	does not conduct	does not conduct
Electrical conductivity in liquid (molten) state	does not conduct	conducts	conducts	conducts

The table above refers to the following four substances:

sodium chloride (NaCl), copper(II) bromide ($CuBr_2$),

aluminium (Al), glucose ($C_6H_{12}O_6$)

(a) Use the table to identify the four substances **P, Q, R**, and **S**.

(b) State the type of chemical bonding in substances **P, R**, and **S**.

(c) Explain why substances **R** and **S** do not conduct when solid but do conduct in the molten state.

6. A pupil carried out experiments to investigate what happens during the electrolysis of molten compounds.
   (a) Explain what is meant by electrolysis.
   (b) Name the products at the positive and negative electrode in the electrolysis of each of the following molten compounds.
       (i) magnesium chloride
       (ii) sodium iodide
       (iii) lead bromide
       (iv) calcium oxide

7. A pupil carried out an experiment to investigate the products of the electrolysis of nickel bromide solution.
   (a) Explain why a d.c. supply is used for this experiment.
   (b) Explain what would be seen at the negative electrode.
   (c) Explain what would be seen at the positive electrode.
   (d) Explain why carbon tetrabromide solution cannot be changed in the same way.

8. Water in swimming pools contains dissolved chlorine. The chlorine used for this is produced by the electrolysis of sodium chloride solution.

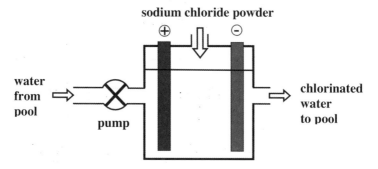

   (a) Why can solid sodium chloride **not** be electrolysed?
   (b) (i) At which electrode is chlorine produced?
       (ii) Describe what is happening in the formation of chlorine.

9. Three bottles are labelled **A**, **B** and **C**.
    Each contained one of the following solutions:
    silver nitrate solution, $AgNO_3$ (aq)
    sodium bromide solution, $NaBr$ (aq)
    ethanol solution, C_2H_5OH (aq)
    The following apparatus can be used to identify the solutions.

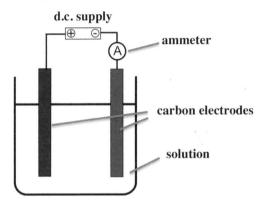

Here are the results for one experiment.

Solution	Meter reading	Observation at negative electrode
A	no	no reaction
B	yes	grey solid formed
C	yes	gas formed

(a) Name the process taking place in the two solutions that conduct.

(b) (i)   Identify solution **A**.

     (ii) What type of bonding must **A** have?

(c) (i)   Identify solution **B**.

     (ii) Explain why the negative electrode turned grey when solution **B** is used.

10. Shown below is a list of compounds and their colours.

sodium chloride	white	sodium sulphate	white
sodium selenate	white	copper sulphate	blue
nickel sulphate	green	vanadium sulphate	violet

State the colour of
(a) copper selenate,
(b) vanadium chloride,
(c) nickel chloride.

11. A crystal of potassium dichromate was placed on moist filter paper at position **X**. When a high voltage was applied an orange colour moved towards the positive electrode.

Explain this observation.

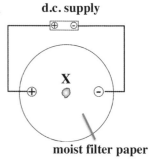

moist filter paper

12.

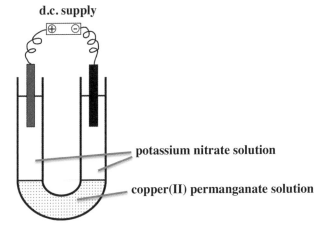

d.c. supply

potassium nitrate solution

copper(II) permanganate solution

The apparatus shown is used to demonstrate the electrolysis of copper permanganate solution.

(a) Why is potassium nitrate solution used instead of water?

(b) Potassium chloride is white while potassium permanganate is purple.

What is the colour of the permanganate ion?

(c) (i) What will be observed after passing the current in the above apparatus for about 20 minutes?

(ii) Explain your answer.

13. A student set up the following experiment.

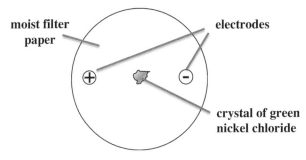

moist filter paper

electrodes

crystal of green nickel chloride

(a) (i) What will happen when the current is switched on?

(ii) Explain your answer.

(b) What will happen if the current is reversed?

14. A student was investigating the electrolysis of molten cadmium iodide.

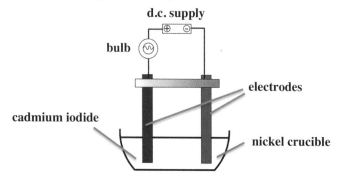

Time	Table 1	Table 2
before heating	bulb not lit	bulb not lit
during heating	bulb lights	bulb lights
when apparatus has cooled	bulb stays lit	bulb goes out

(a) Explain why most groups obtained the results in Table 2.

(b) Name the product formed at each electrode.

(c) Give a possible reason for the faulty results at the end of the experiment in Table **1.**

15. The table below shows the melting point of two chlorides.

Chloride	Melting point /^{o}C
NaCl	801
CCl_4	-23

A student used this information to conclude that ionic bonds are stronger than covalent bonds.

(a) Do you agree with this conclusion?

(b) Explain your answer.

16. Explain each of the following.

(a) Sodium oxide is a solid at room temperature.

(b) Carbon dioxide is a gas at room temperature.

(c) Silicon dioxide is a solid at room temperature.

17. The compounds **P, Q, R** and **S** all contain chlorine. Use the information in the table to answer the questions that follow.
(Assume room temperature to be 25 $^{\circ}$C.)

Chloride	P	Q	R	S
Boiling point /$^{\circ}$C	1690	62	76	1412
Melting point /$^{\circ}$C	1074	-63	-112	708

(a) Which of these chlorides are liquid at room temperature?
(b) State which of these has a molecular structure.

18. Titanium(IV) chloride is a liquid at room temperature.
What does this indicate about the type of bonding in titanium(IV) chloride.

19.   The following table shows the properties of four substances.

Property	P	Q	R	S
appearance	sparkling solid	silvery liquid	white solid	colourless liquid
solubilty in water	insoluble	insoluble	soluble	soluble
electrical conductivity	does not conduct	conducts when solid or molten	conducts when molten or in solution	does not conduct
m.pt / $^{\circ}$C	3547	-61	801	-115
b.pt / $^{\circ}$C	4827	357	1417	59

For each of **P, Q, R** and **S**, explain whether the substance is likely to be a metal, an ionic compound or a covalent compound (molecular or network).

Chemical equations

1. Write the chemical formula for each of the following substances.
    Add the state symbol to show whether the substance is a solid, liquid, gas
    or in solution.

    (a) liquid carbon tetrachloride   (b) carbon dioxide gas
    (c) oxygen gas   (d) silicon oxide solid
    (e) solid sulphur   (f) iodine solid
    (g) a solution of sodium chloride   (h) a solution of sulphur dioxide
         in water   in water

2. Write word equations for each of the following chemical reactions.

    (a) When magnesium metal burns, it reacts with oxygen of the air to
         form magnesium oxide, a white powder.
    (b) In the Blast furnace, iron is made by reacting iron oxide with
         carbon monoxide gas. Carbon dioxide gas is also produced.
    (c) In our bodies, starch which we get from food, breaks down to form
         glucose, which can pass through the walls of our intestines, and water.
    (d) When calcium metal is added to water, a gas is given off and calcium
         hydroxide solution is formed. When tested with a burning splint, the
         gas burns with a "pop".
    (e) Copper oxide powder and a gas that turns limewater milky are made
         when copper carbonate powder is heated.

3. Write a sentence to describe the following reactions.
    The first one is done for you.

    (a) $C(s)$ + $O_2(g)$ → $CO_2(g)$

    Carbon solid reacts with oxygen gas to form carbon dioxide gas.

    (b) $CO(g)$ + $O_2(g)$ → $CO_2(g)$
    (c) $H_2(g)$ + $F_2(g)$ → $HF(g)$
    (d) $SO_2(g)$ + $O_2(g)$ → $SO_3(g)$
    (e) $CuO(s)$ + $CO(g)$ → $Cu(s)$ + $CO_2(g)$
    (f) $NH_3(g)$ → $N_2(g)$ + $H_2(g)$
    (g) $Mg(s)$ + $CO_2(g)$ → $MgO(s)$ + $C(s)$
    (h) $HBr(g)$ → $H_2(g)$ + $Br_2(l)$

4. Balance each of the following equations.

(a) C $+$ O_2 $\rightarrow$ CO_2

(b) P $+$ Cl_2 $\rightarrow$ PCl_3

(c) C $+$ Br_2 $\rightarrow$ CBr_4

(d) C_4H_8 $+$ O_2 $\rightarrow$ CO_2 $+$ H_2O

(e) H_2O_2 $\rightarrow$ H_2O $+$ O_2

(f) $SiCl_4$ $+$ H_2 $\rightarrow$ Si $+$ HCl

5. Balance each of the following equations.

(a) Ca $+$ O_2 $\rightarrow$ CaO

(b) Mg $+$ $AgNO_3$ $\rightarrow$ $Mg(NO_3)_2$ $+$ Ag

(c) NaOH $+$ H_2SO_4 $\rightarrow$ Na_2SO_4 $+$ H_2O

(d) $AgNO_3$ $+$ $BaCl_2$ $\rightarrow$ $Ba(NO_3)_2$ $+$ AgCl

(e) Na $+$ H_2O $\rightarrow$ NaOH $+$ H_2

(f) Al $+$ Cl_2 $\rightarrow$ $AlCl_3$

(g) Ag $+$ O_2 $+$ H_2S $\rightarrow$ Ag_2S $+$ H_2O

(h) Ag_2S $+$ Al $\rightarrow$ Ag $+$ Al_2S_3

(i) HCl $+$ $Na_2S_2O_3$ $\rightarrow$ NaCl $+$ S $+$ SO_2 $+$ H_2O

(j) $TiCl_4$ $+$ H_2O $\rightarrow$ TiO_2 $+$ HCl

6. Write balanced chemical equations for each of the following reactions. State symbols are **not** necessary.

(a) carbon monoxide $+$ oxygen $\rightarrow$ carbon dioxide

(b) hydrogen $+$ chlorine $\rightarrow$ hydrogen chloride

(c) methane (CH_4) $+$ oxygen $\rightarrow$ carbon dioxide $+$ water

(d) sulphur dioxide $+$ oxygen $\rightarrow$ sulphur trioxide

(e) phosphorus $+$ bromine $\rightarrow$ phosphorus bromide

7. Write balanced chemical equations for each of the following reactions. State symbols are **not** necessary.
    (a) sodium   +   oxygen   ➜   sodium oxide
    (b) magnesium   +   sulphur dioxide   ➜   magnesium oxide   + sulphur
    (c) calcium   +   water   ➜   calcium hydroxide   +   hydrogen
    (d) magnesium   +   nitrogen   ➜   magnesium nitride
    (e) barium hydroxide   +   ammonium chloride
            ➜   nitrogen hydride   +   barium chloride   +   water

8. Write balanced chemical equations for each of the following reactions. State symbols are **not** necessary.
    (a) the formation of sulphur trioxide from sulphur dioxide and oxygen
    (b) the combination of methane (CH_4) with chlorine to form carbon tetrachloride
    (c) the burning of camping GAZ (C_3H_8) in plenty of air
    (d) the reaction of nitrogen hydride with oxygen to form nitrogen and water
    (e) the combustion of acetylene (C_2H_2) to form carbon dioxide and water
    (f) the decomposition of nitrogen hydride

Calculations

1. Calculate the formula mass of each of the following substances.
   - (a) H_2O
   - (b) CH_4
   - (c) $CaCO_3$
   - (d) Na_2SO_4
   - (e) $Mg(NO_3)_2$
   - (f) nitrogen hydride
   - (g) carbon dioxide
   - (h) potassium carbonate
   - (i) aluminium oxide
   - (j) ammonium chloride

2. Calculate the mass of one mole of each of the following substances.
   - (a) C_3H_6
   - (b) MgO
   - (c) K_2CO_3
   - (d) $C_6H_{12}O_6$
   - (e) $(NH_4)_3SO_4$
   - (f) magnesium chloride
   - (g) calcium oxide
   - (h) potassium hydroxide
   - (i) magnesium sulphate
   - (j) sodium nitrate

3. Calculate the mass of each of the following substances.
   - (a) 2 mol of sodium
   - (b) 0. 1 mol of $CaSO_4$
   - (c) 0.25 mol of $Mg(NO_3)_2$
   - (d) 5 mol of sulphur dioxide
   - (e) 0.2 mol of magnesium iodide
   - (f) 0.5 mol of ammonium carbonate

4. Calculate the number of moles in each of the following substances.
   - (a) 36 g of carbon
   - (b) 5.6 g of CO
   - (c) 5.6 g of KOH
   - (d) 2.2 g of lithium sulphate
   - (e) 8.2 g of calcium nitrate
   - (f) 5.3 kg of sodium carbonate

5. The composition by mass of a gold ring is shown in the pie chart. The gold ring weighs 7.88 g.

   Calculate the number of moles of gold in the ring.

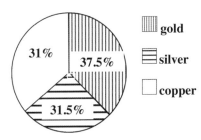

6. Heavy water is made up of molecules in which each of the hydrogen atoms has one neutron in its nucleus.

    Calculate the number of moles of heavy water molecules in 500 g of heavy water.

7. The filling for a tooth is often made of dental amalgam.
    The pie chart shows the composition of a typical dental amalgam.

    (a) Calculate the number of moles of mercury in 2.0 g of dental amalgam.

    (b) Calculate the number of moles of tin in 5.0 g of dental amalgam.

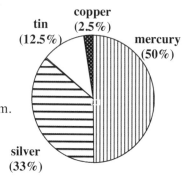

8. Calculate the number of moles of potassium hydroxide that must be dissolved to make each of the following solutions.

    (a) 500 cm^3 of 1 mol l^{-1}

    (b) 200 cm^3 of 0. 5 mol l^{-1}

    (c) 100 cm^3 of 0. 1 mol l^{-1}

    (d) 2 litres of 0.25 mol l^{-1}

    (e) 200 cm^3 of 2 mol l^{-1}

9. Calculate the concentration of each of the following solutions of hydrochloric acid.

    (a) 1 mol of hydrogen chloride dissolved to make 100 cm^3 of solution

    (b) 2.5 mol of hydrogen chloride dissolved to make 1 litre of solution

    (c) 0.1 mol of hydrogen chloride dissolved to make 500 cm^3 of solution

    (d) 0.2 mol of hydrogen chloride dissolved to make 250 cm^3 of solution

    (e) 0.4 mol of hydrogen chloride dissolved to make 200 cm^3 of solution

10. Calculate the volume of each of the following solutions of sodium hydroxide.

(a) 1 mol l^{-1} solution containing 0.2 mol of solute

(b) 0.5 mol l^{-1} solution containing 1 mol of solute

(c) 2 mol l^{-1} solution containing 0.1 mol of solute

(d) 0.1 mol l^{-1} solution containing 0.5 mol of solute

(e) 0.4 mol l^{-1} solution containing 0.1 mol of solute.

11. Calculate the number of grams of substance required to make each of the following solutions. .

(a) 50 cm^3 of NaOH (aq), concentration 2 mol l^{-1}

(b) 100 cm^3 of KOH (aq), concentration 0.5 mol l^{-1}

(c) 1 litre of Na_2CO_3 (aq), concentration 0.1 mol l^{-1}

(d) 25 cm^3 of lithium nitrate solution, concentration 0.2 mol l^{-1}

(e) 250 cm^3 of ammonium sulphate solution, concentration 1 mol l^{-1}

(f) 200 cm^3 of calcium nitrate solution, concentration 0.25 mol l^{-1}

12. Calculate the concentration of each of the following solutions.

(a) 5.85 g of NaCl dissolved to make 1 litre of solution

(b) 1.38 g of K_2CO_3 dissolved to make 100 cm^3 of solution

(c) 8 g of NaOH dissolved to make 250 cm^3 of solution

(d) 2.02 g of potassium nitrate dissolved to make 50 cm^3 of solution

(e) 0.22 g of lithium sulphate dissolved to make 100 cm^3 of solution

(f) 1.27 g of iron(II) chloride dissolved to make 2 litres of solution

Acids and bases

1. (a) (i)   Name **three** laboratory acids.
        (ii) Name **three** 'everyday' solutions that are acidic.
    (b) (i)   Name **three** laboratory alkalis.
        (ii) Name **three** household products that contain an alkali.

2   (a) What is meant by the pH of a solution?
    (b) Name the indicator used to measure the pH of aqueous solutions.
    (c) State the colour changes that can be seen when pH paper is added to
        (i)   acids,
        (ii) alkalis.
    (d) State the range of pH values that can be shown by
        (i)   acids,
        (ii) alkalis.
    (e) (i)   What colour do neutral solutions turn pH paper?
        (ii) What is the pH of water (and neutral solutions)?

3. Decide whether or not each of the following statements
    is **TRUE** or **FALSE**.
    (a) An acid can have a pH of 3.7
    (b) An alkali can have a pH of 14.2
    (c) An acid can have a pH of 0.
    (d) Solutions with a pH between 6 and 8 are neutral.
    (e) An acid can have a pH of -1.
    (f) A solution with a pH of 4 is less acidic than a solution with a pH of 6.
    (g) A solution with a pH of 11 is less alkaline than a solution with a pH
        of 9.

4. Explain why crystals of citric acid have no effect on dry pH paper but turn
    Universal indicator red.

5. Many pollution problems are linked to acid rain.
    (a) (i)   What is meant by acid rain?
        (ii) How is it formed?
    (b) Describe the damaging effects of acid rain on
        (i)   the natural environment,
        (ii) structures and buildings,
        (iii) humans.
    (c) Describe **two** ways of reducing the problems caused by acid rain pollution.

6. Consider the following list of oxides:

    iron(III) oxide,   *sodium oxide,*   *carbon dioxide,*
    calcium oxide,   *nitrogen dioxide,*   *copper(II) oxide,*
    barium oxide,   *nickel oxide,*   *phosphorus oxide*

    (a) Name the **three** oxides that dissolve to produce a solution with a pH below 7.
    (b) Name the **three** oxides that dissolve to produce a solution with a pH above 7.
    (c) Name the **three** oxides that do **not** change the pH of water.

7. Two unknown elements **A** and **B** form oxides. The oxide of **A** gives an aqueous solution of pH 5 while the oxide of **B** gives a solution of pH 10. State what this indicates about
    (a) the oxides of **A** and **B**,
    (b) the elements **A** and **B**.

8. The graph shows the relationship between the solubility of carbon dioxide in water and the temperature of the water.

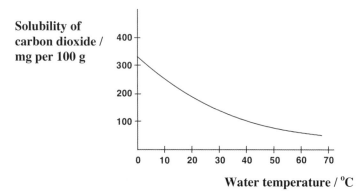

Solubility of carbon dioxide / mg per 100 g

Water temperature / °C

(a) Describe the relationship shown by the graph.

(b) (i) What will happen to the pH when the solution is heated?

(ii) Explain your answer.

9. Using the apparatus shown, a student electrolysed an acid solution.

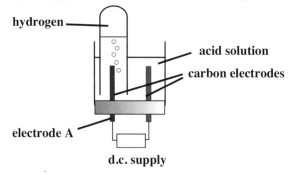

hydrogen

acid solution

carbon electrodes

electrode A

d.c. supply

A gas was observed to be given off at electrode **A**.

(a) What test would show that the gas collected is hydrogen?

(b) (i) Is **A** the positive or negative electrode?

(ii) Explain your answer.

10. Some battery acid is spilt on the garage floor. Water is added before it is wiped up.

    (a) Why is water added?

    (b) What happens to the pH of the solution when water is added?

11. (a) Chlorine reacts with water.

    $$Cl_2 \text{ (g)} + H_2O \text{ (l)} \rightarrow 2H^+ \text{(aq)} + OCl^- \text{(aq)} + Cl^- \text{(aq)}$$

    What happens to the pH of water when it is chlorinated?

    (b) Chromium(VI) oxide also reacts with water.

    $$CrO_3 \text{ (s)} + H_2O \text{ (l)} \rightarrow 2H^+ \text{(aq)} + CrO_4^{2-} \text{(aq)}$$

    What is unusual about the reaction between chromium(VI) oxide and water.

12. A patient who was undergoing heart surgery had the concentration of carbon dioxide and the pH of his blood measured continuously.

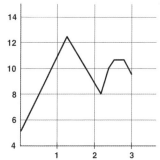
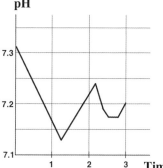

    (a) What happens to the acidity of his blood during the first hour?

    (b) How does the change in concentration of carbon dioxide in his blood affect the pH?

    (c) Carbon dioxide reacts with water.

    $$CO_2 \text{ (g)} + H_2O \text{ (l)} \rightarrow H^+ \text{(aq)} + HCO_3^- \text{(aq)}$$

    How does the equation explain the effect of an increase in concentration of carbon dioxide on the pH of blood?

13. The migration of ions was studied using the apparatus below.

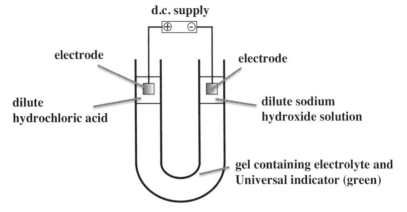

Explain, in terms of movement of ions, the colour changes that would have been observed.

14. (a) What is meant by a base?
(b) Which of the following bases do **not** form an alkali when added to water?

(i) sodium carbonate   (ii) nickel hydroxide
(iii) lithium oxide   (iv) tin(II) hydroxide
(v) barium oxide   (vi) copper(II) carbonate

(c) Why can potassium hydroxide solution be described as '**BOTH** a base and an alkali' and yet copper(II) oxide can be described as 'a base but **NOT** an alkali'?

15. Water, H_2O, can be expected to be made up of molecules with atoms joined by covalent bonds.
(a) Why does water conduct electricity?
(b) Why is the conductivity very poor?

16. Pure water is added to a solution with a pH of 12.
(a) Which **two** ions are present in pure water?
(b) Which contains more hydroxide ions, the solution or the pure water?
(c) What happens to the concentration of hydroxide ions in the solution as the water is added?

17. Acid solutions contain H^+(aq) ions; so does pure water.

   (a) Explain why pure water is **not** an acid.

   (b) When water is added to an acid solution the pH rises.

       (i) Explain why this happens.

      (ii) What is the highest value to which the pH can rise?

     (iii) Explain your answer to (ii).

Reactions of acids

1. (a) Explain what is meant by a neutralisation reaction.
   (b) What happens to the pH of an acid as it is neutralised?
   (e) What happens to the pH of an alkali as it is neutralised?

2. (a) Explain why gardeners add lime to soil that is acidic.
   (b) Explain why Milk of Magnesia is taken to relieve acid indigestion.

3. In certain hard-water areas, scale can build up on the inside of kettles. When tested with Universal indicator, the scale shows a pH above 7.
   (a) Explain why vinegar could be used to descale kettles.
   (b) Name the kind of reaction that would occur.

4. During manned flights in space rockets, carbon dioxide builds up in the air inside the cabin.
   Explain why the rockets also carry a supply of lithium hydroxide.

5. Name the salt that would be formed in the reaction between each of the following solutions.
   (a) potassium hydroxide and nitric acid
   (b) sodium hydroxide and sulphuric acid
   (c) lithium hydroxide and hydrochloric acid

6. Name the acid and the alkali that could be used to prepare solutions of each of the following salts.
   (a) sodium chloride
   (b) potassium sulphate
   (c) barium nitrate

7. (a) (i) Which gas is produced when a metal carbonate reacts with a dilute acid?
   (ii) Describe the test for this gas.
   (b) Name the products of each of the following reactions.
   (i) calcium carbonate and dilute sulphuric acid
   (ii) sodium carbonate and dilute nitric acid

8. Crystals of magnesium sulphate can be made by adding excess magnesium oxide to dilute sulphuric acid.
   (a) Name the kind of reaction which takes place.
   (b) What happens to the pH of the dilute acid as the crystals are added?
   (c) Describe how the excess magnesium oxide can be removed from the solution.
   (d) Write a balanced equation for the reaction taking place.

9. An experiment was carried out on a substance **X**.

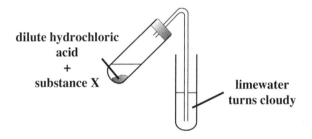

dilute hydrochloric
acid
+
substance X

limewater
turns cloudy

   (a) Which gas turns limewater cloudy?
   (b) From this experiment, what can be learned about **X**?

10.

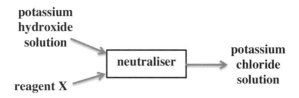

potassium
hydroxide
solution

reagent X

neutraliser → potassium
chloride
solution

(a) Name reagent **X**.
(b) Describe how to produce a dry sample of potassium chloride from a
    neutral solution.

11. Sodium nitrate and sodium carbonate are both white solids.

    Given a sample of each, describe a test you could carry out to discover
    which was which. (Give the results of the test.)

12. Sulphuric acid from a car battery was spilled on the garage floor. First
    water was poured over the acid. Then washing soda (sodium carbonate)
    was sprinkled on it before mopping it up.
    (a) Name the type of reaction that takes place when washing soda is
        added to sulphuric acid.
    (b) Name the gas produced in the reaction.
    (c) Write a balanced equation for the reaction taking place.

13. A student investigated the
    reaction of magnesium and
    dilute sulphuric acid as
    shown in the diagram.

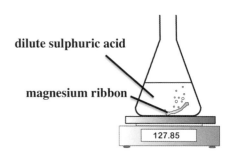

dilute sulphuric acid

magnesium ribbon

127.85

    (a) Why did the reading on the balance fall during the reaction?
    (b) Write a balanced equation for the reaction taking place.

14. Indigestion is caused by too much hydrochloric acid in the stomach.
An indigestion tablet can be taken to reduce the concentration of acid.
The active ingredient in the tablet is magnesium hydroxide.

(a) Describe an experiment that could be carried out to show that the
tablet is effective in reducing the concentration of acid.

(b) (i) Which **two** products are formed when magnesium hydroxide
reacts with hydrochloric acid?

(ii) Name this kind of reaction.

15. Jack prepared copper(II) sulphate by adding excess solid copper(II) oxide
to sulphuric acid.

Jill prepared sodium chloride by the addition of sodium hydroxide solution
to hydrochloric acid.

Explain why Jack and Jill used different methods to prepare their salts.

16. Carbon monoxide can be prepared, in a fume cupboard, by passing carbon
dioxide over heated carbon.

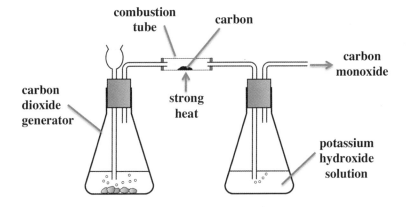

(a) Name **two** chemicals that can be used in the carbon dioxide generator.

(b) What is the purpose of the potassium hydroxide solution?

17. The first step in the procedure to prepare crystals of copper(II) sulphate is shown.

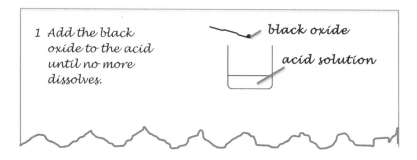

1 Add the black oxide to the acid until no more dissolves.

black oxide

acid solution

(a) Name the black oxide and the acid solution.

(b) Name the type of chemical reaction that took place in the beaker.

(c) Write a balanced equation for the reaction.

18. A student used the instructions on a workcard.

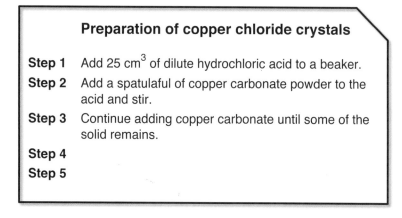

Preparation of copper chloride crystals

Step 1 Add 25 cm^3 of dilute hydrochloric acid to a beaker.

Step 2 Add a spatulaful of copper carbonate powder to the acid and stir.

Step 3 Continue adding copper carbonate until some of the solid remains.

Step 4

Step 5

(a) Why did the student continue to add copper carbonate until some of solid remained?

(b) Name the **two** techniques that the student carried out in steps 4 and 5 to prepare a sample of copper chloride crystals.

(c) Write a balanced equation for the reaction.

19. Identify the **two** spectator ions in each of the following reactions.

(a) Na^+ (aq) + OH^- (aq) + H^+ (aq) + Cl^- (aq)

$\rightarrow$ Na^+ (aq) + Cl^- (aq) + H_2O (l)

(b) $2K^+$ (aq) + CO_3^{2-} (aq) + $2H^+$ (aq) + $2NO_3^-$ (aq)

$\rightarrow$ $2K^+$ (aq) + $2NO_3^-$ (aq) + H_2O (l) + CO_2 (g)

20. For each of the following reactions:

* identify the **two** spectator ions,

* remove the spectator ions to write the ion equation.

(a) $2KOH$ (aq) + H_2SO_4 (aq) $\rightarrow$ K_2SO_4 (aq) + $2H_2O$ (l)

(b) Na_2CO_3 (aq) + $2HNO_3$ (aq) $\rightarrow$ $2NaNO_3$ (aq) + CO_2 (g) + H_2O (l)

Precipitation

1. An insoluble product can be formed in the reaction between solutions.
    (a) Name this kind of reaction.
    (b) Identify the insoluble product in each of the following reactions.
        (i)   potassium sulphate solution and barium nitrate solution
        (ii) calcium chloride solution and sodium carbonate solution
        (iii) potassium hydroxide solution and iron(III) nitrate solution
        (iv) lithium bromide solution and silver nitrate solution

2. Barium carbonate has a solubility of less than $1 \ gl^{-1}$.
    (a) From the following list of substances, select **two** that together could be use to make barium carbonate:
        barium,   barium nitrate,   magnesium carbonate,
        carbon,   barium oxide,   sodium carbonate
    (b) Describe in detail how you would use these two substances to prepare a dry sample of barium carbonate.

3. A class investigated the formation of precipitates.
    A few drops of sodium hydroxide solution were added to four other solutions.

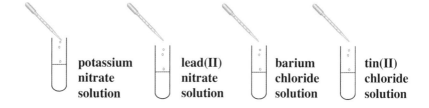

potassium nitrate solution	lead(II) nitrate solution	barium chloride solution	tin(II) chloride solution

    (a) What is meant by a precipitate?
    (b) Identify the solutions that will form a precipitate with sodium hydroxide solution.

4. Sodium sulphate solution and barium chloride solution were mixed as shown.

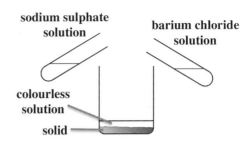

(a) Name the white solid.
(b) Name the technique which could be used to remove the white solid from the solution.

5. Magnesium ions can be removed from magnesium sulphate solution by adding sodium hydroxide solution.

$$Mg^{2+} (aq) \quad + \quad SO_4^{2-} (aq) \quad + \quad 2Na^+ (aq) \quad + \quad 2OH^- (aq)$$

$$\downarrow$$

$$Mg^{2+}(OH^-)_2 (s) \quad + \quad 2Na^+ (aq) \quad + \quad SO_4^{2-} (aq)$$

(a) Name the type of reaction taking place between the magnesium sulphate solution and the sodium hydroxide solution.
(b) Identify the spectator ions in the reaction.

6. When a student added a few drops of sodium chloride solution to silver nitrate solution, a solid formed at the bottom of the beaker.

(a) What is the name of the solid?
(b) Name the spectator ions in the reaction.

7. Patients with stomach problems are given barium sulphate in the form of a "barium meal" before being X-rayed.
   This salt can be prepared in the laboratory by a precipitation reaction.
   (a) Name **two** solutions that could be mixed to prepare barium sulphate.
   (b) Barium compounds are toxic.
      Suggest why people can drink "barium meals" without suffering any ill effects.

8. For each of the following reactions:
   * identify the **two** spectator ions,
   * remove the spectator ions to write the ion equation.

   (a) K_2CO_3 (aq)   + $CuCl_2$ (aq) ➔ $CuCO_3$ (s)   +   2KCl (aq)

   (b) $Ba(NO_3)_2$ (aq) + K_2SO_4 (aq) ➔ $BaSO_4$ (s)   + $2KNO_3$ (aq)

   (c) $AgNO_3$ (aq)   +   LiBr (aq) ➔   AgBr (s)   + $LiNO_3$ (aq)

Volumetric titrations

1. In an investigation to find the concentration of alkali in a water sample, a student carried out three titrations.

    The following results were obtained.

Titration	Volume of acid used / cm^3
1	27.7
2	26.8
3	27.0

    One of the titrations can be described as a **rough** titration.

    (a) What is meant by the underlined word?

    (b) How would the student know when to stop adding acid from the burette?

    (c) What volume of acid would be used in the calculation to find the concentration of alkali?

2. The equation for the reaction between sodium hydroxide solution and dilute hydrochloric acid is:

    $$NaOH\,(aq) \quad + \quad HCl\,(aq) \quad \rightarrow \quad NaCl\,(aq) \quad + \quad H_2O\,(l)$$

    In one titration, 25 cm^3 of sodium hydroxide solution (concentration 0.1 mol l^{-1}) was neutralised by 37.4 cm^3 of a dilute acid.

    (a) Calculate the number of moles of sodium hydroxide used in the titration.

    (b) Calculate the concentration of the dilute hydrochloric acid.

3. Vinegar is a dilute solution of ethanoic acid in water. A student carried out a titration, using 0.1 mol l^{-1} sodium hydroxide solution, to find out the concentration of ethanoic acid in some vinegar.
The average volume of sodium hydroxide solution that was used to neutralise 25 cm^3 of vinegar was 20 cm^3.

(a) Calculate the number of moles of sodium hydroxide in this average volume.

(b) **One** mole of ethanoic acid reacts with **one** mole of sodium hydroxide. Calculate the concentration of ethanoic acid, in mol l^{-1}, in the vinegar.

4. (a)   HCl (aq)   +   NaOH (aq)   ➔   NaCl (aq)   + H_2O (l)
What volume of hydrochloric acid (concentration 0.1 mol l^{-1}) is required to neutralise 50 cm^3 of sodium hydroxide solution (concentration 0.2 mol l^{-1})?

(b) H_2SO_4 (aq)   +   2KOH (aq)   ➔ K_2SO_4 (aq)   + $2H_2O$ (l)
What is the concentration of sulphuric acid if 50 cm^3 neutralises 25 cm^3 of potassium hydroxide solution (concentration 1 mol l^{-1})?

5. (a) What is the concentration of hydrochloric acid if 12.6 cm^3 neutralises 20 cm^3 of potassium hydroxide solution (concentration 0.1 mol l^{-1})?

(b) What volume of nitric acid (concentration 2 mol l^{-1}) is required to neutralise 20 cm^3 of sodium hydroxide solution (concentration 0.5 mol l^{-1})?

(c) What is the concentration of sulphuric acid if 17.3 cm^3 neutralises 25 cm^3 of sodium hydroxide solution (concentration 0.5 mol l^{-1})?

6. A student wanted to prepare ammonium sulphate.

   0.5 mol l^{-1} sulphuric acid was added from a burette to 20 cm^3 of 0.5 mol l^{-1} ammonia solution in a conical flask with pH indicator.

   The equation for the reaction is:

   $2NH_3$ (aq)   + H_2SO_4 (aq)   → $(NH_4)_2SO_4$ (aq)

   (a) Calculate the volume of sulphuric acid that was used to neutralise the ammonia solution.

   (b) The indicator was removed from the ammonium sulphate solution by filtering the solution through charcoal.

   How would the student then obtain a sample of solid ammonium sulphate from the solution?

7. The concentration of dissolved calcium ions in hard water can be found by titration with an acid called EDTA, using a suitable indicator.

   One mole of calcium ions reacts with **one** mole of EDTA.

   In one titration 18.6 cm^3 of 0.12 mol l^{-1} EDTA reacted with 25.0 cm^3 of a water sample.

   Calculate the concentration of calcium ions, in mol l^{-1}, in the sample.

8. The mass of iron present in a piece of wire was determined as shown.

Step 1. The wire was added to excess dilute sulphuric acid. This produced a solution of iron(II) sulphate, $FeSO_4$.

Step 2. The volume of potassium permanganate solution needed to react with the iron(II) sulphate solution by titration was measured.

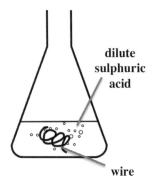

dilute sulphuric acid

wire

(a) Why was the wire reacted with sulphuric acid in Step 1?

(b) It was found that 20.2 cm³ of potassium permanganate solution, concentration 0.15 mol l⁻¹, was needed to react with the iron(II) sulphate solution.

   (i) How many moles of potassium permanganate were needed to react with the iron(II) sulphate solution?

  (ii) **One** mole of potassium permanganate reacts with **five** moles of iron(II) sulphate.

     Calculate the mass of iron present in the steel wire.

Fuels

1*. Petrol is an important **fuel**.
The **combustion** of petrol is an example of an **exothermic** reaction.
Explain what is meant by each of the terms underlined.

2*. Butane is a hydrocarbon; heat is produced when the gas burns.
   (a) Explain what is meant by a hydrocarbon?
   (b) What term is used to describe a reaction that produces heat?
   (c) Which gas is used up when the gas burns?
   (d) What are the **two** products when the gas burns in plenty of air?
   (e) Explain why it is dangerous to burn the gas in a very poorly ventilated room.

3*. The burning of petrol can cause pollution of the air.
   (a) Name the poisonous gas that is formed
      (i) by the incomplete combustion of petrol,
      (ii) from sulphur compounds when petrol is burned,
      (iii) by the sparking of air in a car engine.
   (b) Explain why air pollution is more of a problem in industrial areas.

4*. Powdered limestone (calcium carbonate) is used to remove sulphur dioxide from the gases given off in a coal fired power station.
Limestone is insoluble in water. A soluble carbonate would be more efficient.
   (a) Why should sulphur dioxide be removed?
   (b) Suggest why limestone is used rather than a soluble carbonate.

5*. Biomass is a renewable source of energy. As well as being used directly as a fuel, biomass material can be used to produce biofuels.

    (a) Explain what is meant by

        (i) biomass,

        (ii) a renewable source of energy.

    (b) Give **three** renewable sources of energy.

    (c) Other than biomass, give an example of the use of biomass material as a fuel.

    (d) Name a biofuel and state how it can be produced.

6*. Tree management in our forests is important. Organised felling of trees help to save our finite sources of energy.

    (a) What is meant by a finite source of energy?

    (b) Why can felling trees help to save our finite sources of energy?

7*. Carbon dioxide is one of the important greenhouse gases.

    (a) What is meant by a greenhouse gas?

    (b) Why are levels of carbon dioxide gas in the atmosphere significantly higher in the industrial areas of the world?

8*. Fires in coal mines can be caused by coal dust.

    (a) Which element in air is needed for the coal dust to burn?

    (b) In a limited supply of air, coal fires can produce a poisonous gas. Name this gas.

9*. Catalytic converters in cars can help to reduce carbon monoxide pollution. On the catalyst surface carbon monoxide reacts to form carbon dioxide.

ceramic material covered with catalyst

(a) Why does burning petrol in a car engine produce carbon monoxide as well as carbon dioxide?

(b) Give another way by which carbon monoxide levels from a car engine can be reduced.

10*. Air pollution from the burning of petrol in a car engine can be reduced by using special exhaust systems and improving the efficiency of combustion.

(a) Describe how an exhaust system can be altered so that pollutant gases react to form harmless gases.

(b) Describe how to improve the efficiency of combustion.

11*. The following graph shows how the concentration of carbon monoxide in car exhaust fumes varies with the air to fuel ratio of the mixture that is burned in the engine.

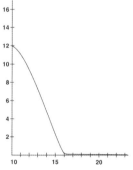

Carbon monoxide /parts per million

Air to fuel ratio

Suggest why the carbon monoxide concentration approaches zero as the air to fuel ratio increases.

12*. Many important fuels are obtained from crude oil.

(a) Describe how crude oil is formed.

(b) Explain why crude oil can be described as a fossil fuel.

(c) Give **two** examples of pollution problems associated with oil.

13*. Crude oil is a mixture of chemical compounds. Before the compounds can be used, the crude oil must be separated into fractions, by fractional distillation.

(a) Name the kind of chemical compounds found in crude oil.

(b) Explain what is meant by

    (i)   fractional distillation,

    (ii) a fraction.

(c) Give a use for each of the following fuels obtained from oil.

    (i)   petrol   (ii) diesel   (iii) gas

    (iv) kerosene   (v) bitumen

14*. (a) Explain what is meant by

    (i)   a flammable substance,

    (ii) a viscous substance.

(b) Name the crude oil fraction that is

    (i)   most flammable,

    (ii) most viscous.

15*. Consider the following fractions obtained from crude oil:

    bitumen,   diesel,   gas,   kerosene,   petrol

(a) Name the fraction that contains molecules with carbon atoms in each of the following ranges.

    (i)   C1 to C4   (ii) C4 to C10   (iii) C9 to C16

    (iv) C15 to C25   (v) more than C25

(b) (i)   Which has the higher boiling point, petrol or diesel?

    (ii) Explain your answer.

Structure of hydrocarbons

1. (a) Explain what is meant by a hydrocarbon.
    (b) In a hydrocarbon, state how many covalent bonds are formed by
       (i) carbon atoms,
       (ii) hydrogen atoms.
    (c) Which of the following carbon compounds are hydrocarbons?
       (i)   heptane, C_7H_{16} (ii)   methylamine, CH_3NH_2
       (iii) glucose, $C_6H_{12}O_6$ (iv)   natural gas, CH_4
       (v)   octene, C_8H_{16} (vi)   carbon dioxide, CO_2
       (vii) alcohol, C_2H_5OH (viii) acetylene, C_2H_2

2. (a) Explain what is meant by
       (i) a saturated hydrocarbon,
       (ii) an unsaturated hydrocarbon.
    (b) Consider the following list of hydrocarbons:

    butane,   ethene,   cyclopropane,   octane,
    methane,   pentene,   cyclohexene

    Name the hydrocarbons that are
    (i) saturated,
    (ii) unsaturated.

3. Name each of the following hydrocarbons.

    (a)   (b)

    (c) CH_3-CH_3 (d) $CH_3-CH_2-CH_2-CH=CH_2$

    (e)   (f)

4. For each of the following hydrocarbons
    (i)   draw the **full** structural formula,
    (ii) draw a **shortened** structural formula.
    (a) propene   (b) methane
    (c) cyclopropane   (d) butane
    (e) ethene   (f) cyclooctene

5. State the molecular formula for each of the following hydrocarbons.
    (a) the saturated straight-chain hydrocarbon with 12 carbon atoms per
        molecule
    (b) the unsaturated straight-chain hydrocarbon with 10 carbon atoms per
        molecule
    (c) the saturated cyclic hydrocarbon with 7 carbon atoms per molecule
    (d) octane
    (e) hexene
    (f) cyclopentane

6. (a) Explain what is meant by a homologous series.
    (b) In each of the following lists of hydrocarbons identify the one that is
        in a different homologous series from the others.
        (i)   ethane   butene   methane   octane
        (ii) C_3H_8 CH_4 C_7H_{14} $C_{12}H_{26}$
        (iii) C_2H_4 C_6H_{12} CH_4 C_4H_8

7. The full structural formulae below represent two members of a homologous series of compounds called the cycloalkenes.

cyclobutene   **cyclohexene**

(a) Draw a full structural formula for the cycloalkene with five carbon atoms.

(b) What is the general formula for the cycloalkene series?

8. Methanal, ethanal and propanal are the first three members of a homologous series.

methanal   **ethanal**   **propanal**

(a) Draw the full structural formula for butanal.

(b) Give the general formula for this homologous series.

9. Name each the following hydrocarbons.

(a) $CH_3-CH-CH_2-CH-CH_3$
          | |
         CH_3 CH_3

(b) CH_3
                        |
    $CH_3-CH_2-C-CH_3$
                        |
                       CH_3

(c) CH_3
                    |
$CH_3-CH_2-CH_2-CH-CH_2-CH_3$

(d) CH_3
      |
     $CH-CH_2$
      | |
     CH_2-CH
             |
            CH_3

10. Draw a structural formula for each of the following hydrocarbons.
    (a) 2,2-dimethylhexane
    (b) 2-ethylpentane
    (c) 2,3,5-trimethylhexane
    (d) 1,2-dimethylcyclopentane

11. Name each of the following alkenes.
    (a) $CH_3-CH=CH-CH_2-CH_2-CH_3$

    (b) 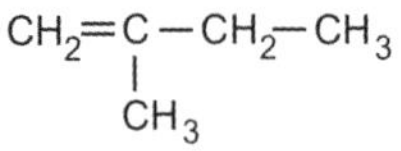 $CH_2=C-CH_2-CH_3$
             |
             CH_3

    (c) CH_3
                |
         $CH_3-C=CH-CH_2-CH_3$

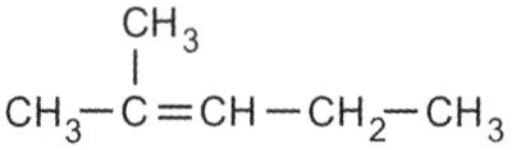

12. Draw a structural formula for each of the following hydrocarbons.
    (a) 2-methylbut-2-ene
    (b) 2,4-dimethylhex-3-ene
    (c) 3,5-dimethylcyclohexene

13. The alkynes are a homologous series of hydrocarbons that contain a carbon to carbon triple bond.

ethyne 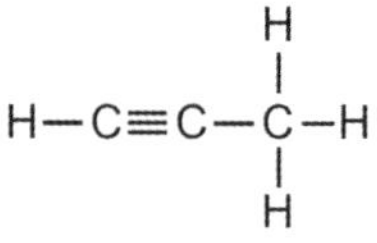   propyne 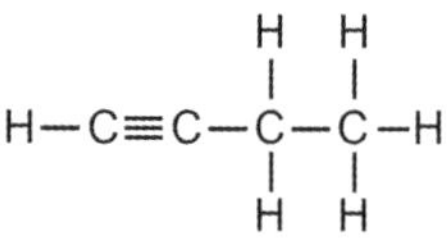   but-1-yne

    (a) Draw the full structural formula for
         (i)   pent-1-yne,
         (ii) pent-2-yne.
    (b) Give the general formula for this homologous series.

Reactions of hydrocarbons

1*. (a) Explain what is meant by cracking.
   (b) (i) What is the purpose of the catalyst in catalytic cracking?
       (ii) Name a catalyst that can be used in the lab.

2*. For each of the cracking reactions shown in the equations below, write the formula and give the name for the hydrocarbons **A** to **E**.

   (a) C_6H_{14} ➜ C_3H_6 +   **A**
   (b) C_7H_{16} ➜ C_4H_{10} +   **B**
   (c) $C_{12}H_{26}$ ➜ C_6H_{12} +   **C**
   (d) $C_{10}H_{22}$ ➜ C_4H_{10} + C_2H_4 +   **D**
   (e) C_7H_{16} ➜ C_2H_6 + C_3H_8 +   **E**

3*. A liquid hydrocarbon is used in two different experiments.
   (a) In Experiment 1, the hydrocarbon has no immediate effect on bromine water.
       What does this indicate?
   (b) The hydrocarbon is used as shown in Experiment 2 below.

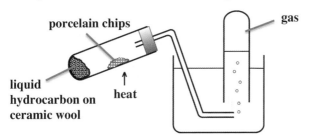

   (i) The gas collected rapidly decolourises bromine water.
       Why is this?
   (ii) Name the chemical reaction occurring in the heated tube.
   (iii) As soon as heating is stopped what precaution must be taken?
        Explain why this is necessary.

4*. The cracking of paraffin can be carried out in the lab using strong heat. A mixture of saturated and unsaturated products is obtained.

   (a) What effect would a suitable catalyst have on the level of heat needed to crack paraffin?

   (b) Explain why cracking produces a mixture of saturated and unsaturated products.

5. Unsaturated hydrocarbons are present in white spirit.

   Describe how you would test white spirit to show that it contains unsaturated hydrocarbons.

6. C_2H_4 + Br_2 →   X

   (a) Draw the full structural formula for substance **X**.
   (b) What name is given to this type of chemical reaction?
   (c) Name the product of the reaction of C_2H_4 with hydrogen.

7. C_3H_6 + Br_2 → $C_3H_6Br_2$

   (a) Is the hydrocarbon C_3H_6 saturated or unsaturated?
   (b) Draw the full structural formula for the product of the reaction.
   (c) Write the molecular formula for the product of the reaction of C_3H_6 with hydrogen.

8. Three different hydrocarbons were treated with bromine solution. Each of the hydrocarbons contained six carbon atoms. The results are shown.

Formula	Hydrocarbon	Effect of bromine
C_6H_{12}	A	Decolourises quickly
C_6H_{14}	B	No immediate change
C_6H_{12}	C	No immediate change

Give the names and draw possible structures for **A**, **B** and **C**.

9. Write the molecular formula for the product of the complete reaction of each of the following hydrocarbons with bromine.

(a) buta-1,3-diene $CH_2{=}CH{-}CH{=}CH_2$

(b) terpinolene

$CH_3{-}C\overset{\displaystyle CH - CH_2}{\underset{\displaystyle CH_2{-}CH_2}{\Big\langle}}C{=}C\overset{\displaystyle CH_3}{\underset{\displaystyle CH_3}{\Big\langle}}$

Isomers

1. (a) Explain what is meant by isomers.
   (b) Illustrate your answer by drawing isomers of butane.

2. Draw the full structural formulae for each of the following.
   (a) **three** isomers of pentane
   (b) **five** isomers of C_4H_8.

3. The full structural formula for three compounds are shown below.

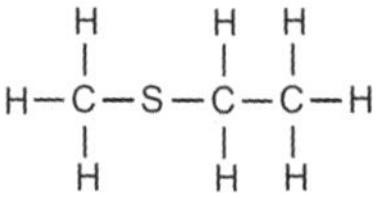

   A 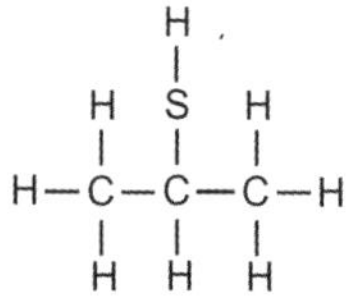   B 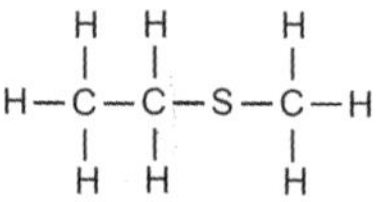   C

   (a) Why can compound **B** be described as an isomer of compound **A**?
   (b) Why is compound **C** **not** an isomer of compound **A**?

4. State whether or not each of the following pairs of molecules are isomers.

   (a)

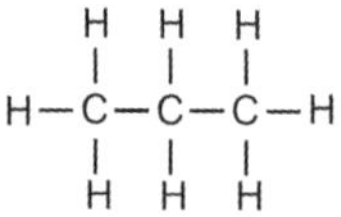

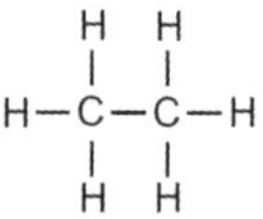

   (b)

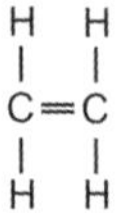

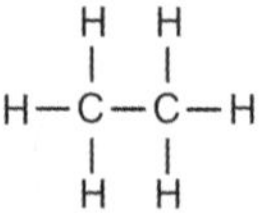

   (c)

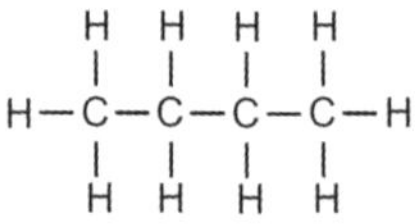

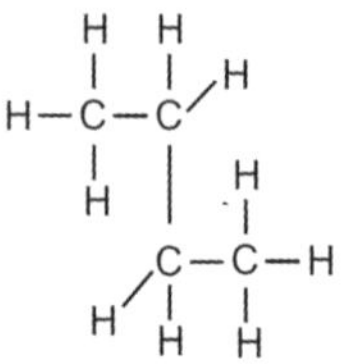

(d)

```
    H   H   H   H
    |   |   |   |
H — C — C — C — C — H
    |   |   |   |
    H       H   H
    H — C — H
        |
        H
```

```
    H   H   H
    |   |   |
H — C — C — C — H
    |   |   |
    H       H
    H — C — H
        |
    H — C — H
        |
        H
```

(e)

```
    H   H
    |   |   H
H — C — C
    |   |   H   H
    H   |   |   |
        C — C — C — H
       /    |   |   |
      H     H   H   H
```

```
        H
        |
    H — C — H
        H
    H — C
        |   H   H
        |   |   |
       C — C — C — H
      /    |   |   |
     H     H   H   H
```

(f)

```
    H   H
    |   |
H — C — C — H
    |   |
H — C — C — H
    |   |
    H   H
```

```
    H       H   H   H
     \      |   |   |
      C = C — C — C — H
     /          |   |
    H           H   H
```

(g)

```
        H
        |
    H — C — H
        H   H
        |   |
H — C — C — C — H
    |   |   |
    H   H   H
    H — C — H
        |
        H
```

```
    H   H   H   H
    |   |   |   |
H — C — C — C — C — H
    |   |   |   |
    H   H       H
        H — C — H
            |
            H
```

(h)

```
    H       H
     \     /
      C
     / \
H — C — C — H
    |   |
    H   H
```

```
    H   H   H
    |   |   |
H — C — C — C — H
    |   |   |
    H   H   H
```

(i)

```
    H       H   H   H
     \      |   |   |
      C = C — C — C — H
     /          |   |
    H           H   H
```

```
    H   H   H
    |   |   |       H
H — C — C — C = C
    |   |          \
    H   H           H
```

(j)

```
    H       H   H   H
     \      |   |   |
      C = C — C — C — H
     /          |   |
    H           H   H
```

```
    H   H   H   H
    |   |   |   |
H — C — C = C — C — H
    |           |
    H           H
```

5. State whether or not each of the following pairs of hydrocarbons are isomers.

    (a) 2-methylbutane   butane

    (b) 2,3-dimethylhexane   octane

    (c) 3-methylhexane   3-methylpentane

    (d) 2-methylpent-1-ene   hex-2-ene

    (e) pent-1-ene   methylcyclobutane

6. State whether or not each of the following pairs of molecules are isomers.

7. Hexa-1,3-diene is a hydrocarbon that contains two double bonds per molecule.

hexa-1,3-diene

$$\underset{H}{\overset{H}{\diagup}}C=\underset{H}{\overset{H}{C}}-\overset{H}{\underset{H}{C}}=\underset{H}{\overset{H}{C}}-\underset{H}{\overset{H}{C}}-\underset{H}{\overset{H}{C}}-H$$

Draw the full structural formula for an isomer of hexa-1,3-diene that

(a) contains **two** double bonds per molecule,

(b) contains **only** one double bond per molecule.

Patterns in carbon componds

1. A student carried out three experiments with each of the following carbon compounds.

$$H-\overset{\overset{\displaystyle H}{|}}{\underset{\underset{\displaystyle H}{|}}{C}}-\overset{\overset{\displaystyle H}{|}}{\underset{\underset{\displaystyle H}{|}}{C}}-\overset{\overset{\displaystyle H}{|}}{\underset{\underset{\displaystyle H}{|}}{C}}-OH$$

A

B

C

The results are shown.

Compound	Reaction with sodium	Effect on acidified potassium permanganate	Flammability
A	gas produced	goes colourless	flammable
B	no reaction	goes colourless	flammable
C	no reaction	none	flammable

(a) From the results, what general statement can be made about all three compounds?

(b) From the results, describe how to distinguish
   (i) **A** from **B**,
   (ii) **B** from **C**.

(c) Predict what will happen when acidified potassium permanganate is added to the compound with the structure shown.

2. A way of grading types of petrol is to use 'octane numbers'.

Hydrocarbon	Octane number
H−C−C−C−C−C−C−C−C−H (octane chain, 8 carbons, all with H)	-10
H−C−C−C−C−C−C−C−H (7 carbon chain, all with H)	0
H−C−C−C−C−C−C−C−H with H−C−H branch below second carbon	23
H−C−C−C−C−C−C−H (6 carbon chain, all with H)	25
H−C−C−C−C−C−H with two H−C−H branches below	83
H−C−C−C−C−C−H with H−C−H branch above and two H−C−H branches below	100

State **two** features of the molecular structure that give a high octane number.

3. The hydrocarbons present in a mixture can be separated by passing through a special column. Different hydrocarbons move through the column at different speeds.

The following graph was obtained for one mixture.

1 $CH_3{-}CH_3$ **2** $CH_3{-}\underset{\underset{\textstyle CH_3}{|}}{CH}{-}CH_3$ **4** $CH_3{-}\underset{\underset{\textstyle CH_3}{|}}{\overset{\overset{\textstyle CH_3}{|}}{C}}{-}CH_3$

3 $CH_3{-}CH_2{-}CH_2{-}CH_3$

5 $CH_3{-}CH_2{-}\underset{\underset{\textstyle CH_3}{|}}{\overset{\overset{\textstyle CH_3}{|}}{CH_2}}{-}CH_3$

6 $CH_3{-}CH_2{-}CH_2{-}CH_2{-}CH_3$

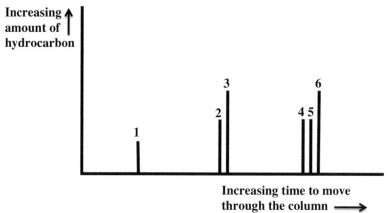

(a) Make **two** general statements linking the molecular structure of the hydrocarbon with the length of time taken to pass through the column.

(b) Copy the graph and show with an arrow, the expected position for propane.

4. Iodoalkanes are alkane molecules with a hydrogen atom replaced by an iodine atom. The reaction of iodoalkanes with sodium produces alkanes. e.g. ethane can be made from iodomethane.

```
    H                    H              H  H
    |                    |              |  |
H — C — I  + 2Na  +  I — C — H  →  H — C — C — H  +  2NaI
    |                    |              |  |
    H                    H              H  H
iodomethane                             ethane
```

(a) Name the alkane that forms when sodium reacts with iodoethane.
(b) Name the **two** iodoalkanes used to make propane.
(c) This type of reaction can also be used to make cycloalkanes.
   Draw a structural formula for the compound that could be used to make cyclohexane.

5. The following reaction shows what happens when an alkene reacts with ozone.

```
    H  H  H  H  H      ozone     H  H  H           H  H
    |  |  |  |  |        →       |  |  |           |  |
H — C — C — C = C — C — H    H — C — C — C = O   O = C — C — H
    |  |       |                |  |                   |
    H  H       H                H  H                   H
```

(a) Draw the full structural formulae for the products from the following reaction.

```
    H  H  H  H  H  H  H      ozone
    |  |  |  |  |  |  |        →
H — C — C = C — C — C — C — C — H
    |  |       |  |  |  |
    H  H       H  H  H  H
```

(b) Ozonolysis of alkenes can result in only **one** product.
   Draw the full structural formula for an alkene that would react in this way.

6. Organic chemistry has a number of rules that can help to predict the products of a reaction.

   The equation shows what happens when an ionic compound in solution is added to an alkene.

$$\begin{array}{ccc} \overset{\displaystyle H}{\underset{\displaystyle H}{\overset{|}{\underset{|}{C}}}} = \overset{\displaystyle H}{\underset{\displaystyle CH_3}{\overset{|}{\underset{|}{C}}}} & + \quad H^+Br^- \ (aq) \quad \rightarrow & H - \overset{\displaystyle H}{\underset{\displaystyle H}{\overset{|}{\underset{|}{C}}}} - \overset{\displaystyle H}{\underset{\displaystyle CH_3}{\overset{|}{\underset{|}{C}}}} - Br \end{array}$$

   The positive ion adds on to the double-bonded carbon atom that has the greater number of hydrogen atoms bonded to it.

   (a)

$$\overset{\displaystyle H}{\underset{\displaystyle H}{\overset{|}{\underset{|}{C}}}} = \overset{\displaystyle CH_3}{\underset{\displaystyle CH_3}{\overset{|}{\underset{|}{C}}}} \quad + \quad HO^+Cl^- \ (aq) \quad \rightarrow$$

   Draw a structural formula for the product in the above reaction.

   (b) Draw a structural formula for an isomer of butene that could **not** be used to demonstrate the above rule.

7. Alkenes can be made by the reaction of a carbon-oxygen compound with a phosphorus compound.

$$\begin{array}{cccc} \overset{\displaystyle R_1}{\underset{\displaystyle R_2}{\overset{|}{\underset{|}{C}}}} = O & + \ \ C_6H_5 - \overset{\displaystyle C_6H_5}{\underset{\displaystyle C_6H_5}{\overset{|}{\underset{|}{P}}}} = \overset{\displaystyle R_3}{\underset{\displaystyle R_4}{\overset{|}{\underset{|}{C}}}} \ \rightarrow & \overset{\displaystyle R_1}{\underset{\displaystyle R_2}{\overset{|}{\underset{|}{C}}}} = \overset{\displaystyle R_3}{\underset{\displaystyle R_4}{\overset{|}{\underset{|}{C}}}} & + \ \ C_6H_5 - \overset{\displaystyle C_6H_5}{\underset{\displaystyle C_6H_5}{\overset{|}{\underset{|}{P}}}} = O \end{array}$$

   R is a shorthand way of writing a hydrogen atom or an alkane with one hydrogen atom removed,

   e.g. –R could be –H, -CH$_3$, -C$_2$H$_5$, -C$_3$H$_7$, etc

   (a) Draw a structural formula for the alkene formed in the following reaction.

$$\begin{array}{cc} \overset{\displaystyle CH_3}{\underset{\displaystyle CH_3}{\overset{|}{\underset{|}{C}}}} = O & + \ \ C_6H_5 - \overset{\displaystyle C_6H_5}{\underset{\displaystyle C_6H_5}{\overset{|}{\underset{|}{P}}}} = \overset{\displaystyle H}{\underset{\displaystyle CH_3}{\overset{|}{\underset{|}{C}}}} \quad \rightarrow \end{array}$$

   (b) Draw a structural formula for the carbon-oxygen compound that would be used to make ethene.

8. Haloalkanes are alkane molecules with a hydrogen atom replaced by a halogen atom.

The name of the haloalkane depends on the position of the halogen atom in the molecule.

1-chlorobutane   2-bromobutane

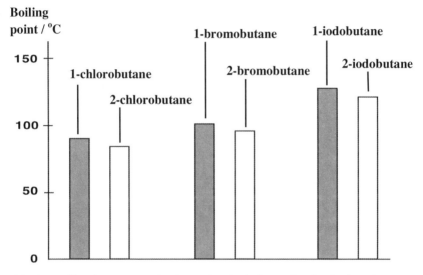

(a) Describe the **two** trends shown by the information in the bar chart.
(b) Draw the full structural formula for
    (i)   3-iodopentane,
    (ii) 1-chloropropane.

Carbohydrates

1*. (a) Name **three** foodstuffs that contain a carbohydrate.
   (b) Name the **three** elements that are present in carbohydrates.
   (c) What kind of bonding is found in carbohydrates.

2*. Which of the following compounds are carbohydrates?
   (a) glucose, $C_6H_{12}O_6$
   (b) acetone, C_3H_6O
   (c) carbon monoxide, CO
   (d) hexane, C_6H_{12}
   (e) sucrose, $C_{12}H_{22}O_{11}$
   (f) water, H_2O
   (g) alcohol, C_2H_5OH

3*. A spoonful of sugar is burned in air. It is then placed in a jar of oxygen.
   (a) What difference will be observed in the burning?
   (b) What are the products of the reaction?

4*. The diagram represents the process by which energy is produced in animals.

X

energy

water

carbohydrate A

Y

   (a) Name the process.
   (b) Name carbohydrate **A**.
   (c) Name gases **X** and **Y**.
   (d) Give **three** examples of how the energy produced can be used by animals.

5*. Plants make glucose by photosynthesis.

    (a) Identify gases **X** and **Y**.

    (b) To which family of compounds does glucose belong?

    (c) Name the substance, stored in plants, that is made when glucose units join together.

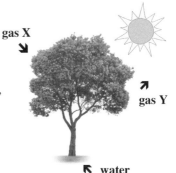

gas X

gas Y

↖ water

6*. Carbohydrates are energy-containing foods.

    (a) Where does this energy come from?

    (b) Write a word equation to show what happens when glucose combines with oxygen in our bodies.

7*. The flow diagram below shows an important process that occurs in green plants.

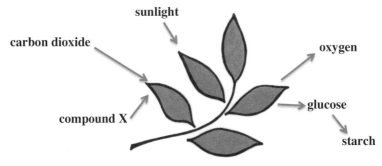

sunlight

carbon dioxide

oxygen

compound X

glucose

starch

chlorophyll in plant leaf

    (a) Name the process.

    (b) What is the purpose of the chlorophyll?

    (c) Name compound **X**.

    (d) What kind of reaction occurs in the change from glucose to starch?

8*. The flow chart shows part of the carbon cycle.

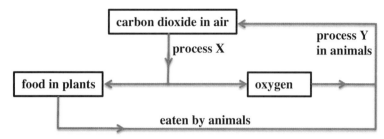

(a) Name processes **X** and **Y**.

(b) The amount of carbon dioxide entering the air has increased considerably in the last 50 years.

Suggest a reason for this increase.

(c) In recent years, many countries have cleared extensive areas of forest for the development of towns and industry.

Explain why this presents dangers to life on earth.

9*. The table shows the relationship between the temperature of sea water and the amount of dissolved oxygen.

Temperature of water /°C	0	20	40	60	70	80
Concentration of dissolved oxygen / grams in each cubic metre	69.4	43.4	30.8	22.7	18.6	13.8

(a) State the relationship between the solubility of oxygen in sea water and the temperature of the water.

(b) Suggest why Arctic seas support a lot more animal life than might be expected.

10*. Starch and glucose are both carbohydrates.

(a) What is the ratio of hydrogen to oxygen atoms in a carbohydrate?

(b) Why does glucose dissolve easily in water and yet starch does not?

(c) Explain what is seen when a beam of light is passed through

(i) glucose solution,

(ii) starch in water.

11*. Starch and glucose are both white solids.
  (a) (i)   What solution can be used to test for starch?
      (ii) What is the colour change that takes place when the test is positive?
  (b) (i)   What solution can be used to test for glucose?
      (ii) What is the colour change that takes place when the test is positive?
      (iii) Why is a water bath used to heat the solution?

12*. A carbohydrate was tested as shown below.

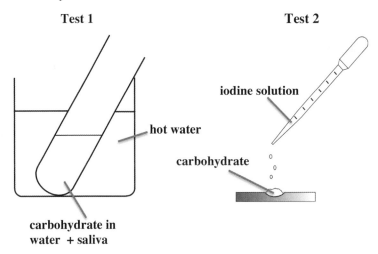

Test 1   **Test 2**

iodine solution

hot water

carbohydrate

carbohydrate in
water + saliva

Result: **Result:**
After the solution was neutralised,   Iodine solution turned
Benedict's solution gave an orange   blue/black.
precipitate.

  (a) Name the carbohydrate used in Tests 1 and 2.
  (b) Name the carbohydrate produced by the reaction in Test 1.
  (c) What kind of substance, present in saliva, was responsible for the result in Test 1?

13*. Carbohydrates supply the body with energy.

Explain why eating a Mars bar (containing glucose) just before a race might be of more value to an athlete than eating bread (containing starch).

14*. (a) Give the approximate alcohol content (in units) of each of the following.

(i)   pint of beer/lager   (ii) single measure of spirit

(iii) small glass of wine   (iv) bottle of alcopop

(v) large glass of wine

(b) Describe the effects of alcohol intake.

15*. Alcohol for drinks can be made from carbohydrates.

(a) Name this process.

(b) Name **three** sources of carbohydrates for the production of an alcoholic drink.

(c) Describe briefly how to obtain alcohol from carbohydrates.

16*. Two processes are involved in the manufacture of alcohol for 'spirit' drinks.

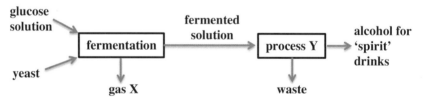

(a) Name gas **X**.

(b) What kind of substance, present in yeast, acts as a catalyst for the reaction?

(c) Name process **Y**.

17*. The production of alcohol from glucose is normally carried out at a temperature around 40 °C.

    (a) (i) Would the reaction be speeded up by increasing the temperature?

       (ii) Explain your answer.

    (b) Explain why there is a limit to the concentration of alcohol obtained in this reaction.

18*. Yeast is used in making bread, a food rich in carbohydrate. Alcohol is made from a source of carbohydrate; yeast contains an enzyme needed for this reaction.

Why does eating bread **not** lead to the body making alcohol?

19*. An enzyme is most efficient under optimum conditions. The effect of changing pH and temperature for one particular enzyme, **A**, is shown below.

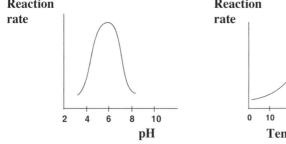

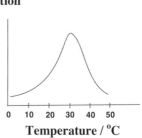

    (a) What is meant by the optimum conditions for an enzyme?

    (b) For enzyme **A**, state

       (i) the optimum pH,

       (ii) the optimum temperature.

    (c) Why do enzymes in the human body have an optimum temperature of about 37 °C?

Alcohols

1. Give the systematic name for each of the following alcohols.

    (a) CH_3-CH_2-OH

    (b)
    $$CH_3-\underset{\underset{OH}{|}}{CH}-CH_2-CH_3$$

    (c)
    $$CH_3-CH_2-\underset{\underset{OH}{|}}{\overset{\overset{CH_3}{|}}{C}}-CH_3$$

    (d)
    $$CH_3-\underset{\underset{OH}{|}}{CH}-CH_2-\overset{\overset{CH_3}{|}}{CH}-CH_3$$

2. Draw a structural formula for each of the following alcohols.

    (a) butan-l-ol

    (b) hexan-3-ol

    (c) 3-methylpentan-l-ol

    (d) 3,3-dimethylbutan-2-ol

3. Two isomeric straight-chain alcohols, each having four carbon atoms, are known.

    (a) Draw a structural formula for each of these alcohols.

    (b) Draw a structural formula for each of the **two** isomeric branched-chain alcohols.

4. Ethane-1,2-diol is a dihydric alcohol used as anti-freeze for car cooling systems.

    ethane-1,2-diol
    $$\underset{\underset{OH}{|}}{CH_2}-\underset{\underset{OH}{|}}{CH_2}$$

    (a) Suggest what is meant by a dihydric alcohol.

    (b) Draw the full structural formula for propane-1,2,3-triol.

    (c) Give another **two** uses for alcohols other than for alcoholic drinks.

5. Alcohols can be oxidised by hot copper(II) oxide.
   The product is either an aldehyde or a ketone.

Alcohol	Structural formula	Type of product	Structural formula
ethanol	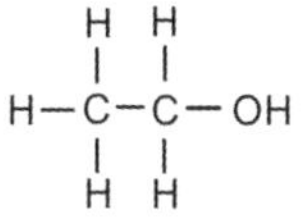 H-C-C-OH (with H,H on each C)	aldehyde	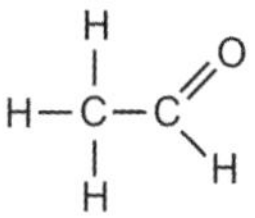 H-C-C with =O and H
propan-1-ol	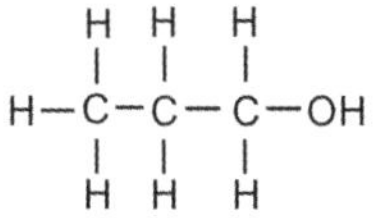 H-C-C-C-OH	aldehyde	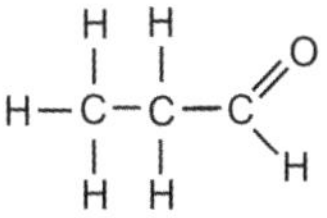 H-C-C-C with =O and H
propan-2-ol	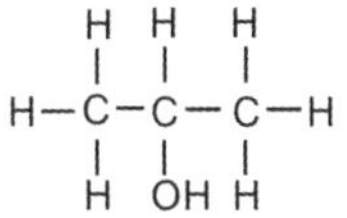 H-C-C-C-H (with OH on middle C)	ketone	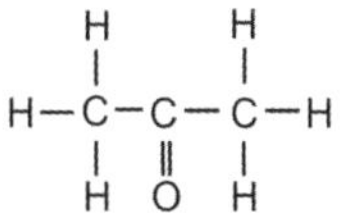 H-C-C-C-H (with =O on middle C)
butan-2-ol	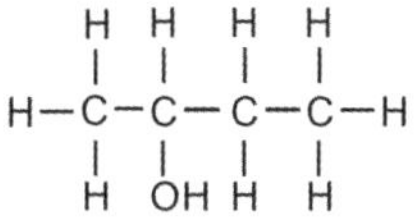 H-C-C-C-C-H (with OH on second C)	ketone	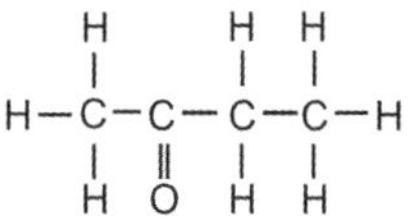 H-C-C-C-C-H (with =O on second C)

(a) Write a general statement linking the type of product to the structure of the alcohol used.

(b) Draw the full structural formula for the carbon compound formed by the oxidation of

   (i) methanol,

   (ii) pentan-1-ol,

   (iii) hexan-3-ol.

6. The product of the reaction between an alkene and a mixture of carbon monoxide and hydrogen is an alcohol.

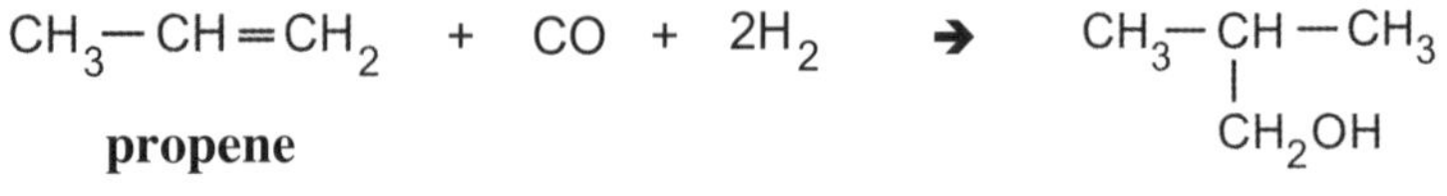

$$CH_3-CH=CH_2 \ + \ CO \ + \ 2H_2 \ \rightarrow \ CH_3-\underset{\underset{CH_2OH}{|}}{CH}-CH_3$$

propene

(a) Name the alcohol formed in the above reaction.

(b) Draw a structural formula for the alkene that would give the following alcohol. $CH_3-\underset{\underset{CH_2OH}{|}}{CH}-CH_2-CH_3$

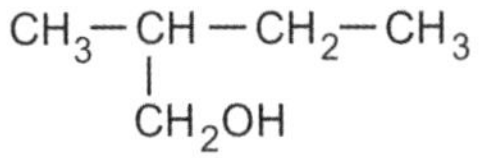

(b) Name the alcohol that would be obtained from ethene.

7. A class carried out a test with a number of carbon compounds.
The results are shown in the table.

Molecule	Structure	Name	Result of test
A	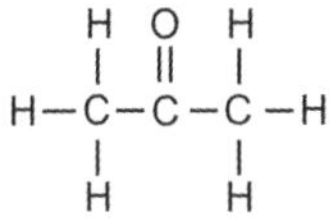 H O H | || | H−C−C−C−H | | H H	propanone	no reaction
B	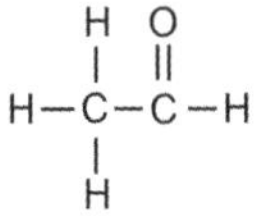 H O | || H−C−C−H | H	ethanal	orange precipitate forms
C	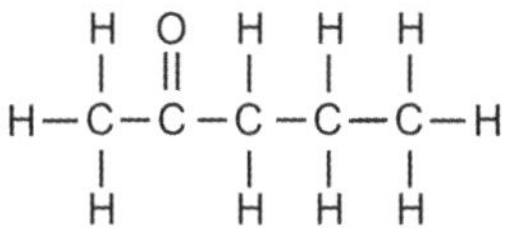 H O H H H | || | | | H−C−C−C−C−C−H | | | | H H H H	pentanone	no reaction
D	O || H−C−H	methanal	orange precipitate forms

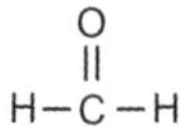

(a) Write a general statement linking the result of the test to the structure of the carbon compound.

(b) State whether or not an orange precipitate will form with the following molecule.

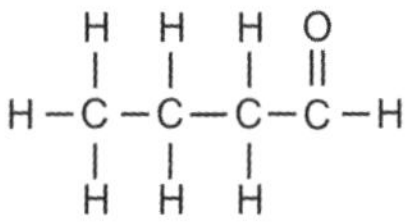

H H H O
\| \| \| \|\|
H−C−C−C−C−H
\| \| \|
H H H

(c) Draw the full structural formula for
(i) butanone,
(ii) propanal.

Carboxylic acids

1. Give the systematic name for each of the following carboxylic acids.

    (a)
    $$CH_3-C\begin{smallmatrix}O\\\\OH\end{smallmatrix}$$

    (b)
    $$H-C\begin{smallmatrix}O\\\\OH\end{smallmatrix}$$

    (c)
    $$CH_3-\underset{\underset{}{\overset{CH_3}{|}}}{CH}-CH_3-C\begin{smallmatrix}O\\\\OH\end{smallmatrix}$$

    (d)
    $$CH_3-CH_2-CH_2-\underset{\underset{CH_3}{|}}{CH}-C\begin{smallmatrix}O\\\\OH\end{smallmatrix}$$

2. Draw a shortened structural formula for each of the following carboxylic acids.

    (a)   propanoic acid
    (b)   3-methylpentanoic acid
    (c)   2-methylhexanoic acid

3. (a)   Draw a structural formula for butanoic acid.
    (b)   Draw a structural formula for an acid that is an isomer of butanoic acid.

4. Vinegar is a solution of a carboxylic acid in water.
    (a)   Name the carboxylic acid used to make vinegar.
    (b)   Give a use for vinegar
        (i)   in the food industry,
        (ii) as a household cleaning product.

Esters

1. Esters are useful compounds. They can be made in the lab.
   (a) (i) Name the catalyst used in the lab preparation of an ester.
       (ii) Why is a Bunsen flame **not** used to heat the reactants?
       (iii) How can the ester be separated from the unreacted alcohol and carboxylic acid?
   (b) Give a use for esters that is related
       (i) to their smell,
       (ii) to their solvent properties.

2. Esters can be made in the lab as described in the workcard shown below

PREPARATION OF AN ESTER.

1. Mix 1 cm^3 of **X** with 1 cm^3 of **Y** in a test tube.
2. Wrap a piece of paper soaked in cold water around the test tube and hold in place as shown in the diagram.
3.

4.

Paper soaked in cold water

Mixture of X and Y

   (a) Describe the distinctive smell of an ester.
   (b) (i) Name the types of carbon compounds, **X** and **Y**, used to make an ester.
       (ii) Give appropriate instructions for Steps 3 and 4 to complete the workcard.
       (iii) What is the purpose of the paper soaked in cold water?

3. Name each of the following esters.

(a)

CH_3-C with $=O$ and $O-CH_3$

(b)

O, $C-H$, CH_3-O

(c)

CH_3-C with $=O$ and $O-CH_2-CH_2-CH_3$

(d)

$H-C$ with $=O$ and $O-CH_2-CH_3$

4. Draw a structural formula for each of the following esters.
   (a) ethyl butanoate   (b) propyl propanoate

5. For each of the following combinations, name the ester that is formed and draw a structural formula.
   (a) ethanol / methanoic acid
   (b) methanol / propanoic acid

   (c) CH_3-CH_2-OH / CH_3-C with $=O$ and OH

   (d) $CH_3-CH_2-CH_2-OH$ / $H-C$ with $=O$ and OH

6 For the breakdown of each of the following esters, name the products and draw their structural formulae.
   (a) ethyl propanoate   (b) methyl ethanoate

   (c) O, $C-H$, CH_3-CH_2-O

   (d) $CH_3-CH_2-CH_2-C$ with $=O$ and $O-CH_3$

7. (a) Draw structural formulae for the **two** esters that are isomers of propanoic acid.
   (b) Name each of the esters.

Energy from fuels

1. (a) Explain what is meant by
      (i) an exothermic reaction,
      (ii) an endothermic reaction.
   (b) Give an example of each.

2. Copy and complete the following:
   During an exothermic reaction, energy is required to ----- bonds in the -----
   molecules. Energy is then ----- as the bonds are formed in the product
   molecules. In this type of reaction, more energy is released in the bond–
   ----- step than is required in the bond- ----- step.

3. The energy released from the burning of different alcohols can be
   compared by calculating the energy released from the burning of one mole
   of each.

Alcohol	Structural formula	Heat released / kJ mol^{-1}
methanol	CH_3OH	727
ethanol	CH_3CH_2OH	1367
propan-1-ol	$CH_3CH_2CH_2OH$	2020

   (a) Make a general statement linking the heat released and the number of
       carbon atoms in the alcohol molecule.
   (b) Suggest why there is a fairly constant difference between the heat
       released per mole for any two successive members of the alcohol
       series.
   (c) Predict the heat released in the burning of one mole of butan-1-ol.
   (d) When calculating the heat energy released in the burning of a fuel in
       the lab, why is the experimental value less than the actual value?

4. For each of the following, calculate the heat energy released by the burning of the fuel.

(a) The temperature of 50 cm³ of water is increased by 15 °C.

(b) The temperature of 100 cm³ of water is increased by 23.6 °C.

(c) The temperature of 150 cm³ of water is increased from 20.9 °C to 39.1 °C

(d) The temperature of 700 cm³ of water is increased from 16.3 °C to 23.1 °C

Calculations based on equations

1. $$Mg\,(s) \quad + \quad Cl_2\,(g) \quad \rightarrow \quad MgCl_2\,(s)$$

    Calculate the mass of magnesium chloride produced in the reaction of 4.9 g of magnesium with excess chlorine.

2. $$CH_4\,(g) \quad + \quad 2O_2\,(g) \quad \rightarrow \quad CO_2\,(g) \quad + \quad 2H_2O\,(g)$$

    Calculate the mass of carbon dioxide produced in the reaction of 3.2 g of methane (CH_4) with excess oxygen.

3. $$4Na\,(s) \quad + \quad 2O_2\,(g) \quad \rightarrow \quad 2Na_2O\,(s)$$

    Calculate the mass of sodium oxide produced in the reaction of 2.3 g of sodium with excess oxygen.

4. $$N_2\,(g) \quad + \quad 3H_2\,(g) \quad \rightarrow \quad 2NH_3\,(g)$$

    Calculate the mass of hydrogen required to react with 56 g of nitrogen.

5. $$4Al\,(s) \quad + \quad 3O_2\,(g) \quad \rightarrow \quad 2Al_2O_3\,(s)$$

    Calculate the mass of oxygen required to react with 2.7 g of aluminium.

6. $$Mg\,(s) \quad + \quad CuSO_4\,(aq) \rightarrow \quad MgSO_4\,(aq) \quad + \quad Cu\,(s)$$

    Calculate the mass of copper produced in the reaction of 9.8 g of magnesium with excess copper(II) sulphate.

7. As a result of recycling, an industrial plant converts 7.7×10^4 kg of hydrogen to ammonia (NH_3) each day.

    $$N_2\,(g) \quad + \quad 3H_2\,(g) \quad \rightarrow \quad 2NH_3\,(g)$$

    Calculate the mass of ammonia that is produced each day.

8. Ammonium sulphate is a fertiliser. The compound can be produced by the reaction of ammonia (NH_3) with sulphuric acid (H_2SO_4).

$$2NH_3\,(g) \quad + \quad H_2SO_4\,(aq) \quad \rightarrow \quad (NH_4)_2SO_4\,(s)$$

Calculate the mass of ammonium sulphate that could be produced from 170 kg of ammonia.

9. Ammonia (NH_3) can be formed by adding water to magnesium nitride.

$$Mg_3N_2\,(s) \quad + \quad 6H_2O\,(l) \quad \rightarrow \quad 3Mg(OH)_2\,(s) \quad + \quad 2NH_3\,(g)$$

Calculate the mass of ammonia produced when 20.3 g of magnesium nitride are added to excess water.

10. A power station produces sulphur dioxide, an atmospheric pollutant. The sulphur dioxide can be removed by reaction with limestone (calcium carbonate).

$$CaCO_3 \quad + \quad SO_2 \quad \rightarrow \quad CaSO_3 \quad + \quad CO_2$$

Calculate the mass of calcium carbonate required to remove completely 320 tonnes of sulphur dioxide.

11. The monomer for polythene can be produced from ethanol.

$$C_2H_5OH \quad \rightarrow \quad C_2H_4 \quad + \quad H_2O$$
$$\text{ethanol} \qquad\qquad \text{ethene} \qquad \text{water}$$

Calculate the maximum mass of ethene that can be produced from 6900 kg of ethanol.

12. Nitrogen is used to fill the air-bags which protect people in car crashes. It is produced when sodium azide (NaN_3) decomposes rapidly.

$$2NaN_3\,(s) \quad \rightarrow \quad 2Na\,(s) \quad + \quad 3N_2\,(g)$$

A driver's air-bag contains 60 g of sodium azide.

Calculate the mass of nitrogen gas that would be produced.

Metals

1.* Aluminium metal is used to make aircraft, cooking pots and pans, window frames and cooking foil.

Copper metal is useful for making electrical wiring, hot and cold water pipes and the bases of cooking pans.

For each metal state **three** properties that make it suitable for these uses.

2.* This country recycles many important metals.
   (a) What is meant by the recycling of metals?
   (b) Explain why there is a need to recycle many metals.

3.* Alloys can be made with very specific properties. Some are very hard, some are resistant to corrosion and some have special magnetic or electrical properties.
   (a) What is meant by an alloy?
   (b) Name **three** alloys and give a use for each.
   (c) Explain why two aluminium/copper alloys can have different strengths.

4.* Wire gauzes on tripod stands in laboratories can be made to last longer by using an alloy of iron.
   (a) Why are alloys of metals made?
   (b) Suggest **two** properties that make alloys of iron a good choice for a wire gauze.

5. The properties of metals are related to the way that the atoms are held together.
   (a) Describe the bonding in a metal.
   (b) Explain why metals conduct electricity.

Reactivity series

1. (a) Name **three** metals that are stored under oil.
   (b) What does this indicate about the reactivity of these metals?

2. The apparatus shown can be
   used to compare the reactivity
   of different metals.

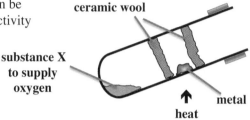

   ceramic wool

   substance X
   to supply
   oxygen

   metal

   heat

   (a) What is the name of substance **X**, used to supply oxygen on heating?
   (b) Why can this experiment be used to compare the reactivity of different
        metals?

3. When sodium metal is added to cold water, the metal melts to form the
   shape of a ball and quickly moves about the surface of the water. Hydrogen
   gas is rapidly produced.
   (a) (i) How can the gas be identified?
       (ii) Explain why the metal melts.
   (b) Name a metal that reacts in the lab more vigorously with water than
        sodium.
   (c) Predict what will happen in the reaction of rubidium with water.

4. (a) Name **two** metals that
        (i) react with dilute hydrochloric acid,
        (ii) do **not** react with dilute hydrochloric acid.
   (b) Which gas is produced in the reaction of a metal with dilute
        hydrochloric acid?
   (c) Name the other product in the reaction of magnesium with
        hydrochloric acid.

5. A student added zinc to dilute sulphuric acid.
    (a) What was the effect on the pH of the acid?
    (b) Write a balanced chemical equation for the reaction.

6. The earliest people on Earth used gold and silver for making jewellery. Other metals like sodium and magnesium were unknown until approximately 200 years ago.
    (a) Explain why gold and silver were among the first metals to be discovered.
    (b) Explain why sodium and magnesium were not discovered until more recent times.

7. Some metals are found **uncombined** in the Earth's crust but most have to be **extracted** from their ores.
    (a) Explain what is meant by each of the terms in bold.
    (b) (i) Name **two** metals that are found uncombined.
        (ii) What can be concluded about the reactivity of metals that are found uncombined?
    (c) Name **two** metals that are extracted from their ores by heating with carbon.

8. A pupil carried out experiments with iron oxide, sodium oxide and silver oxide. On heating the three metal oxides, it was found that one decomposed to form the metal and oxygen gas. On heating with carbon, one of the other two metal oxides reacted to form the metal.
    (a) Which metal oxide would decompose on heating alone?
    (b) Which metal oxide would **not** decompose on heating with carbon?

9. The oxides of metals **X** and **Y** are unaffected by heat but the oxide of **Z** gives off oxygen when it is heated. The oxide of **Y** is stable to heating with carbon but the oxide of **X** decomposes.
    (a) Place the three metals in order of reactivity.
        (Start with the most reactive.)
    (b) Suggest a name for each of the metals **X**, **Y** and **Z**.

10. A pupil was asked to investigate three metal oxides **LO, M₂O** and **NO**. On heating strongly, **LO** broke down into a metal **L** and oxygen. The other two oxides did not break down.

   (a) From this evidence what can be deduced about the reactivity of metal **L**?

   (b) How could you test **M₂O** and **NO** in order to find out which was the more reactive of the metals **M** and **N**?

11. Carbon monoxide can be used to extract iron from iron(III) oxide. Carbon dioxide is produced in the reaction.

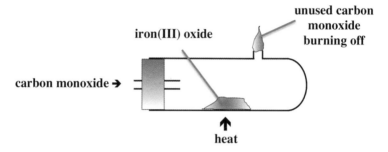

   (a) Write a balanced equation for the reaction that takes place.

   (b) Explain why calcium cannot be extracted from its oxide in this way.

12. The results of experiments with four metals **W**, **X**, **Y** and **Z** and their compounds are summarised in the table below.

Metal	Column 1 Reaction of metal with dilute acid	Column 2 Action of heat on metal oxide	Column 3 Reaction of metal with cold water
W	hydrogen evolved	no reaction	hydrogen formed
X	no reaction	no reaction	no reaction
Y	hydrogen evolved	no reaction	very slow reaction
Z	no reaction	metal formed	no reaction

(a) State what information about the order of reactivity of the metals can be obtained from

   (i)   Column 1 alone,

   (ii) Column 2 alone.

(b) Now use all the information to put the metals into an order of reactivity placing the most reactive first.

(c) Suggest a name for each metal **W**, **X**, **Y** and **Z**.

13. **A**, **B**, **C** and **D** are four metals to be arranged in an order of reactivity.

(a) For each bit of information (i) to (iii), what can be concluded about the relative reactivity of the metals?

   (i)   The oxides of **C** and **D** do not decompose on heating alone, while that of **A** does.

   (ii) **B** reacts with dilute acid to produce hydrogen gas, while **D** does not.

   (iii) **C** reacts quickly with cold water, **B** reacts slowly with cold water.

(b) Use the above information to place the four metals in order of reactivity. (Start with the most reactive.)

(c) Suggest a name for each metal **A**, **B**, **C** and **D**.

14. Information about the metals **M, E, T, A** and **L** and their compounds is listed below.

    (i) With water, **A** reacts vigorously, **M** slowly, **E, T** and **L** do not react.

    (ii) Only the oxide of **E** decomposes by heating alone.

    (iii) Heating with carbon reduces the oxides of **L, E** and **T** but not the other oxides.

    (iv) **M, A** and **L** react with dilute hydrochloric acid while **T** and **E** do not.

    (a) For each bit of information (i) to (iv), what can be concluded about the relative reactivity of the metals?

    (b) Use the above information to place the five metals in order of reactivity (most reactive first).

    (c) When nitrates of these metals are heated only one decomposes to give the metal.

    Which is most likely to do so?

15. Identify the spectator ion in each of the following reactions.

    (a) $2Al\,(s)\ +\ 6H^+\,(aq)\ +\ 6Cl^-\,(aq)$

    $\rightarrow\ 2Al^{3+}\,(aq)\ +\ 6Cl^-\,(aq)\ +\ 3H_2\,(g)$

    (b) $Fe\,(s)\ +\ 2H^+(aq)\ +\ SO_4^{2-}\,(aq)$

    $\rightarrow\ Fe^{2+}(aq)\ +\ SO_4^{2-}\,(aq)\ +\ H_2\,(g)$

16. For each of the following reactions:

    * identify the spectator ion,

    * remove the spectator ion to write the ion equation.

    (a) $Zn\,(s)\ +\ H_2SO_4\,(aq)\ \rightarrow\ ZnSO_4\,(aq)\ +\ H_2\,(g)$

    (b) $Mg\,(s)\ +\ 2HCl\,(aq)\ \rightarrow\ MgCl_2\,(aq)\ +\ H_2\,(g)$

Redox reactions

1. (a) Explain what is meant by
   (i) oxidation,
   (ii) reduction.
   (b) Write an ion-electron equation for each of the following reactions.
   (i) the oxidation of magnesium atoms
   (ii) the reduction of copper(II) ions to copper
   (iii) the oxidation of potassium atoms
   (iv) the reduction of aluminium ions
   (v) the oxidation of chloride ions
   (vi) the reduction of fluorine
   (vii) the oxidation of iron(II) ions
   (viii) the oxidation of sulphite ions

2. (a) What is meant by a redox reaction?
   (b) For each of the following reactions, combine the oxidation and reduction steps to form a balanced redox equation.

   (i) Al (s) $\rightarrow$ Al^{3+} (aq) + $3e^-$
   $2H^+$ (aq) + $2e^-$ $\rightarrow$ H_2 (g)

   (ii) Ce^{4+} (aq) + e^- $\rightarrow$ Ce^{3+} (aq)
   $2Br^-$ (aq) $\rightarrow$ Br_2 (g) + $2e^-$

   (iii) Cu (s) $\rightarrow$ Cu^{2+} (aq) + $2e^-$
   Ag^+ (aq) + e^- $\rightarrow$ Ag (s)

   (iv) MnO_4^- (aq) + $8H^+$ (aq) + $5e^-$ $\rightarrow$ Mn^{2+} (aq) + H_2O (l)
   Fe^{2+} (aq) $\rightarrow$ Fe^{3+} (aq) + e^-

   (v) $Cr_2O_7^{2-}$ (aq) + $14H^+$ (aq) + $6e^-$ $\rightarrow$ Cr^{3+} (aq) + $7H_2O$
   Sn^{2+} (aq) $\rightarrow$ Sn^{4+} (aq) + $2e^-$

(c) For each of the following redox reactions, write an ion-electron equation for the oxidation and reduction steps.

(i) Cl_2 (g) + $2Fe^{2+}$ (aq) → $2Cl^-$ (aq) + $2Fe^{3+}$ (aq)

(ii) Zn (s) + Cu^{2+} (aq) → Zn^{2+} (aq) + Cu (s)

(iii) Mg (s) + $2H^+$ (aq) → Mg^{2+} (aq) + H_2 (g)

(iv) Cl_2 (g) + $2KBr$ (aq) → Br_2 (g) + $2KCl$(aq)

(v) $2Na$ (s) + H_2 (g) → $2NaH$ (s)

3. When iron(III) chloride is added to a solution containing iodide ions, the iron(III) ions are reduced to iron(II) ions.

$$Fe^{3+} (aq) \quad + \quad e^- \quad → \quad Fe^{2+} (aq)$$

(a) Write the ion-electron equation for the oxidation reaction.
(b) Name the kind of reaction that occurs between iron(III) ions and iodide ions.

4. Bromine water is decolourised by sulphite ions.

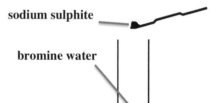
sodium sulphite

bromine water

Write the ion-electron equation to show what happens to
(a) the bromine,
(b) the sulphite ions.

Displacement

1. When magnesium ribbon is added to copper sulphate solution, the ribbon starts to break up at the surface, a brown solid forms, and the solution eventually becomes colourless.
    Magnesium ribbon does **not** react with sodium sulphate solution.
    Explain these observations.

2. When a copper coin is put into silver nitrate solution the coin turns a grey colour. When an identical coin is put into sodium chloride solution the coin did **not** change in any way.
    Explain what was observed in each case.

3. At high temperature, uranium(IV) fluoride is reduced by magnesium metal.

    $$UF_4 \text{ (g)} \quad + \quad 2Mg \text{ (s)} \quad \xrightarrow{1600\,°C} \quad U \text{ (l)} \quad + \quad 2MgF_2 \text{ (l)}$$

    (a) State whether uranium is a more reactive or less reactive metal than magnesium.
    (b) The reaction is an example of a redox reaction.
         Give another name for this kind of reaction.

4. Part of the electrochemical series is shown opposite.
    From its position in the series, state what would happen when metal **X** is added to an aqueous solution of

    (a) copper(II) sulphate,
    (b) magnesium chloride.

magnesium
metal **X**
iron
tin
copper

5. Excess magnesium powder was added to 25 cm^3 of each of four solutions and the change in temperature recorded.

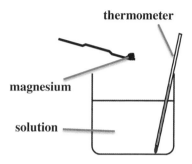

Solution	Temperature / $^{\circ}$C	
	Initial	Final
copper chloride	25	67
iron chloride	25	49
nickel chloride	25	44
zinc chloride	25	39

(a) Write a general statement about the rise in temperature when magnesium displaces other metals from solutions.

(b) State **two** ways to ensure that the investigation was fair.

6. Identify the spectator ion in each of the following reactions.

(a) Mg (s)   +   Cu^{2+} (aq)   +   2Cl$^-$ (aq)

        ➔   Mg^{2+} (aq)   +   Cu (s)   +   2Cl$^-$ (aq)

(b) Zn (s)   +   2Ag$^+$ (aq)   +   2NO$_3^-$ (aq)

        ➔   Zn^{2+} (aq)   +   2Ag (s)   +   2NO$_3^-$ (aq)

(c) The reaction of aluminium with lead(II) nitrate solution.

(d) The reaction of nickel with copper(II) sulphate solution.

7. (a) State whether or not a reaction takes place when each of the metals is added to the solution.
      (i) magnesium added to copper(II) sulphate solution
      (ii) copper added to sodium chloride solution
      (iii) zinc added to silver nitrate solution
      (iv) copper added to zinc sulphate solution
      (v) silver added to copper(II) chloride solution
      (vi) aluminium added to magnesium nitrate solution
   (b) Write ion-electron equations for the oxidation and reduction reactions that occur.

8. A pupil carried out a series of experiments involving the displacement of one metal by another. Four different metals were used and two of them, **P** and **Q** were from unlabelled bottles. Each metal was placed, in turn, in various metal salt solutions.
   The following table shows the results of the experiments. A tick (✓) indicates that a displacement reaction was seen to occur; a cross (✗) indicates that no reaction occurred.

	Solutions			
Metal	zinc sulphate	lead nitrate	copper(II) chloride	silver nitrate
magnesium	✓	✓	✓	✓
copper	✗	✗	✗	✓
p	✗	✓	✓	✓
Q	✓	✓	✓	✓

   (a) Suggest names for metals **P** and **Q** that would give the results shown in the table.
   (b) (i) What would have been the colour of the solution after the reaction of copper with the silver nitrate solution?
      (ii) For this reaction, write the ion-electron equation to show how the copper would have changed.

9. A piece of zinc is added to copper(II) chloride solution.
   (a) State what happens
      (i) to the piece of zinc,
      (ii) to the copper(II) ions,
      (iii) to the colour of the solution.
   (b) Write ion-electron equations for the oxidation and reduction reactions that occur.

Electrochemical cells

1.* One of the most widely used batteries is known as the dry cell. This is used in portable radios, torches and toys.

   (a) Explain why a dry cell eventually has to be replaced.

   (b) What is the purpose of the ammonium chloride paste in a dry cell?

   (c) Explain why the ammonium chloride is in the form of paste and not completely "dry".

   (d) State **one** advantage of a nickel-cadmium battery compared to a dry cell.

2.* The battery in a car is an example of a battery that can be recharged.

   (a) What name is given to this kind of battery?

   (b) What energy change takes place during recharging?

3.* Many portable radios can use electricity from the mains as well as from batteries.

   (a) State **one** advantage of having a radio that has batteries.

   (b) In the house, is it cheaper to run the radio from the mains or the batteries?

4. A simple cell can be made using a lemon and two different metals. The lemon juice is an electrolyte.

   (a) State the direction of the electron flow through the wire.

   (b) What is the purpose of the electrolyte?

   (c) State what would happen to the reading on the voltmeter

      (i) if the iron was replaced with a piece of zinc,

      (ii) if the copper was replaced with a piece of tin.

5. A simple dry cell can be made from everyday materials.

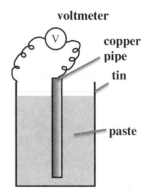

The paste is made from salt (sodium chloride), water and porridge.

Porridge is composed mainly of starch.

(a) State the direction in which electrons flow through the wire.

(b) Name the electrolyte in the paste.

(c) Why could sugar **not** be used as an electrolyte?

6. Refer to the diagram.

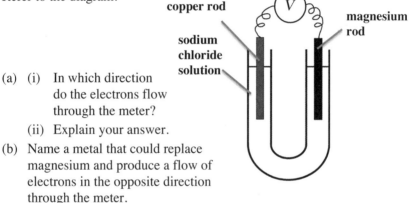

(a) (i) In which direction do the electrons flow through the meter?

   (ii) Explain your answer.

(b) Name a metal that could replace magnesium and produce a flow of electrons in the opposite direction through the meter.

(c) What would happen to the meter reading if the copper rod was replaced by an iron rod?

(d) (i) What would happen to the meter reading if the sodium chloride solution was replaced by sugar solution?

   (ii) Explain your answer.

7. The following diagram shows one of the earliest designs of battery. It is connected to a meter for measuring voltage.

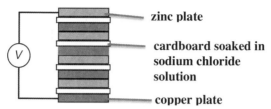

- zinc plate
- cardboard soaked in sodium chloride solution
- copper plate

(a) When the sodium chloride solution is replaced by potassium nitrate solution, a reading is still obtained on the meter. When ethanol is used, no reading is obtained.

Explain each of these results.

(b) State what will happen to the reading on the meter
   (i) if the zinc is replaced by tin,
   (ii) if the copper is replaced by silver.

8.

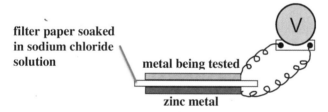

filter paper soaked in sodium chloride solution

metal being tested

zinc metal

Three metals were tested in the experiment above.

The results are shown in the table.

Metal tested	Voltage / V	Direction of electron flow
R	0.3	zinc to metal R
S	0.4	metal S to zinc
T	1.0	zinc to metal T

(a) State which one of the four metals (R, S, T and zinc) is highest in the electrochemical series.

(b) Arrange the four metals in order of their position in the electrochemical series, with the highest first.

9. Using the apparatus below, the following results were obtained.

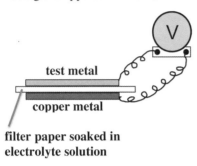

Test metal	Voltmeter reading / V
lithium	2.9
sodium	2.4
magnesium	1.6
iron	0.5
tin	0.4
copper	0.0
silver	-0.4

test metal
copper metal
filter paper soaked in electrolyte solution

(a) What name is given to this kind of series of metals arranged from voltmeter readings?

(b) Suppose the copper metal was replaced by tin metal.
   (i)   What would be the reading on the meter if the test metal is iron?
   (ii) What would be the reading on the meter if the test metal is silver?
   (iii) Which metal could be used as the test metal to give a voltmeter reading of approximately 1.2 V?

(c) Sugar solution cannot be used as the electrolyte.
   What does this indicate about the bonding in sugar?

10. Nicola was given a chemistry set as a birthday present. One of the activities was to use electricity from a chemical reaction to operate a digital stop clock. She made the stop clock work using only the items shown.

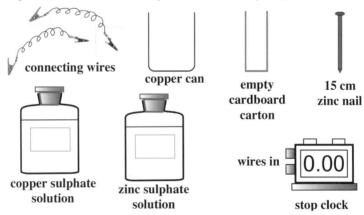

connecting wires
copper can
empty cardboard carton
15 cm zinc nail
copper sulphate solution
zinc sulphate solution
wires in
0.00
stop clock

Draw a labelled diagram to show how Nicola arranged the items.

Chemistry in Society

11.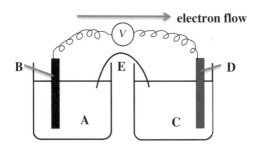
electron flow

(a) Using magnesium, copper, magnesium sulphate solution and copper sulphate solution, state what **A, B, C** and **D** must be to give a flow of electrons in the direction shown.

(b) (i) What is **E** on the diagram known as?

(ii) Why is it necessary?

(c) State the electrode at which

(i) oxidation takes place,

(ii) reduction takes place.

12. The diagram shows a cell set up by a student.

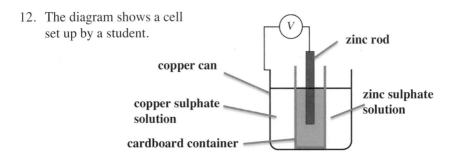

zinc rod

copper can

copper sulphate solution

zinc sulphate solution

cardboard container

(a) (i) State the direction of electron flow through the meter.

(ii) What difference would there be in the meter reading if the zinc was replaced by magnesium and the zinc sulphate solution by magnesium sulphate solution?

(iii) If the cell shown was allowed to run for 24 hours, what visible signs of a chemical change would there be?

(b) In a second experiment, the cardboard container was replaced by a glass beaker.

Explain why the bulb did not light.

13. The arrangement shown is used to produce
    a flow of electrons.

    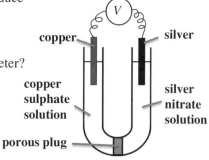

    (a) (i)   In which direction do the
              electrons flow through the meter?
        (ii) Explain your answer.
    (b) Write the ion-electron equation
         for the reaction at each electrode.

14.

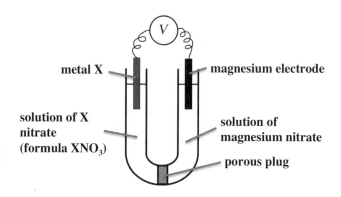

    Oxidation takes place at the magnesium electrode.

    (a) In which direction will electrons flow through the meter?
    (b) Write the ion-electron equation for the reaction at the magnesium
         electrode.
    (c) Which electrode will decrease in mass?
    (d) Write the ion-electron equation for the reaction at electrode **X**.

15.

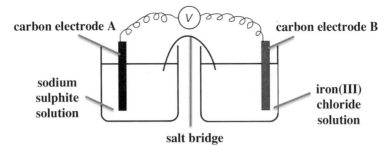

In the cell shown, the electrons flow through the meter from electrode **A** to electrode **B**.

(a) State the electrode at which
   (i) oxidation takes place,
   (ii) reduction takes place.
(b) Write the ion-electron equation for the reaction involving the sulphite ions at electrode **A**.
(c) Explain what happens in the salt bridge.

16.

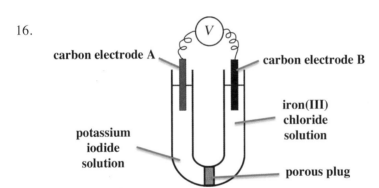

The reaction occuring at electrode **B** is:

$$Fe^{3+} (aq) \quad + \quad e^- \quad \rightarrow \quad Fe^{2+} (aq)$$

(a) Name the type of chemical reaction occurring at electrode **B**.
(b) In which direction do the electrons flow through the meter?
(c) (i) What product will be formed from iodide ions at electrode **A**?
   (ii) Write the ion-electron equation for the reaction at this electrode.

17. Sodium sulphite solution reacts with bromine solution. The sulphite ions are oxidised. The ion-electron equation for the oxidation reaction is:

$$SO_3^{2-} (aq) \quad + \quad H_2O (l) \quad \rightarrow \quad SO_4^{2-} (aq) \quad + \quad 2H^+ (aq) \quad + \quad 2e^-$$

This reaction takes place in the cell shown.

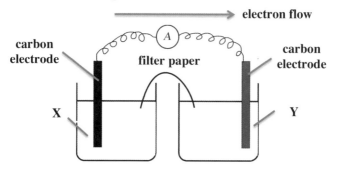

(a) On the diagram, identify the two solutions at **X** and **Y** so that the flow of electrons is in the direction shown.

(b) What is the purpose of the filter paper soaked in electrolyte between the beakers?

(c) Write the ion-electron equation for the reduction reaction.

(d) If samples of the two solutions were mixed, what would you see happening?

18. Electrochemical cells use redox reactions to produce electricity. An example of a cell is shown.

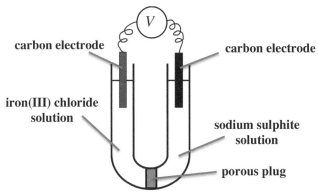

The reaction taking place at electrode **B** of the above cell is:

$$SO_3^{2-} (aq) \quad + \quad H_2O (l) \quad \rightarrow \quad SO_4^{2-} (aq) \quad + \quad 2H^+ (aq) \quad + \quad 2e^-$$

(a) Name the type of reaction taking place at electrode **B**.

(b) State the direction of electron flow through the meter.

(c) As the reaction proceeds at electrode **A**, iron(III) ions react to form iron(II) ions.

    (i) Explain why this happens.

    (ii) Write the ion-electron equation for the reaction at electrode **A**.

19. The cells which power heart pacemakers contain lithium metal.

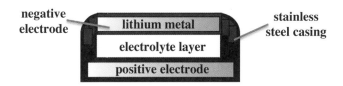

(a) Explain why lithium metal is a good choice for the negative electrode.

(b) What is the purpose of the electrolyte in the cell?

(c) Explain why water is **not** used in the electrolyte layer.

20. A fuel cell is a device that makes electricity. Hydrogen is the most common fuel and the other reactant is usually oxygen.

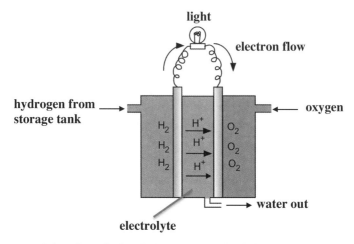

(a) Explain why a fuel cell does not go 'dead' in the same way as a radio battery.

(b) Suggest a possible source of oxygen for use in the cell.

(c) (i) Write the ion-electron equation for the formation of hydrogen ions.

    (ii) Is this an oxidation or reduction reaction?

Using electricity

1. Copper(II) chloride solution is electrolysed in the apparatus shown.

   (a) Why is a d.c. supply used for electrolysis?
   (b) Write ion-electron equations for the formation of
       (i) the solid,
       (ii) the gas.
   (c) Name the kind of reaction taking place at each electrode.

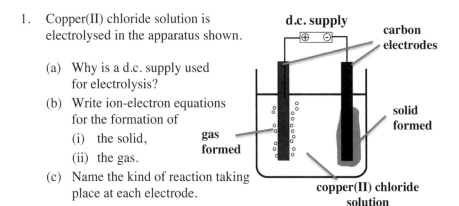

2. Copper can be electroplated with nickel by the electrolysis of nickel(II) chloride solution.

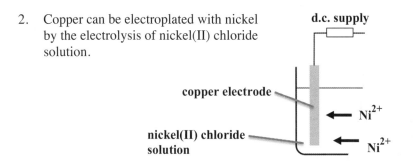

   (a) Write the ion-electron equation for the formation of the nickel.
   (b) Is this an example of oxidation or reduction?
   (c) Does this reaction occur at the positive or negative electrode?

3. Copper can be purified by electro-refining. This process is illustrated in the diagram.

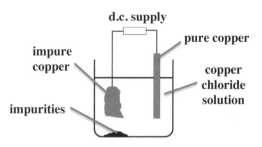

The ion-electron equation for the process occurring at the impure electrode
is: Cu (s)   → Cu^{2+} (aq)   + $2e^-$

(a) What name is given to the kind of reaction at the impure electrode?
(b) Is the impure electrode the positive or the negative electrode?
(c) During electro-refining, what happens to the mass of the pure copper electrode?
(d) Write the ion-electron equation for the reaction at the pure copper electrode.

4.

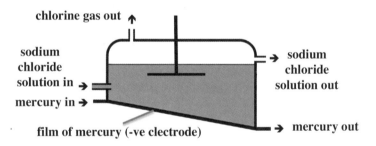

The cell shown is used for the industrial manufacture of chlorine.

(a) In the cell, the sodium chloride is broken up by the electrical energy.
    What name is given to this process?
(b) Name the kind of reaction that occurs at the mercury electrode.
(c) Write the ion-electron equation for what happens at the titanium electrode.
(d) Suggest an advantage in maintaining a continuous flow of sodium chloride solution.

5. The following reactions take place at the electrodes when a solution of common salt is electrolysed.

positive electrode: $2Cl^-$ (aq) $\rightarrow$ Cl_2 (g)   + $2e^-$

negative electrode: $2H_2O$ (l)   + $2e^-$ $\rightarrow$ H_2 (g)   + $2OH^-$ (aq)

(a) Name the type of reaction taking place at the negative electrode.
(b) As the electrolysis continues, explain what will happen to the pH of the salt solution.

6. The lead-acid battery used in cars is an example of a rechargeable battery.

(a) When the battery is being recharged, what name is given to the process taking place?
(b) During this process, state the kind of reaction taking place at
(i)   the negative electrode,
(ii)   the positive electrode.

7. Electricity is used to obtain aluminium from a molten mixture containing aluminum oxide.

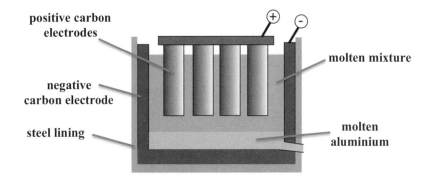

(a) Why does the mixture need to be kept molten?
(b) Explain why aluminium is formed at the negative electrode.
(c) Suggest why the positive electrodes have to be replaced at regular intervals.

8. Anodising involves increasing the thickness of the oxide layer of aluminium.

   (a) Which process is involved in anodising?

   (b) Is the aluminium the positive or negative electrode?

   (c) Give **two** uses for anodised aluminium.

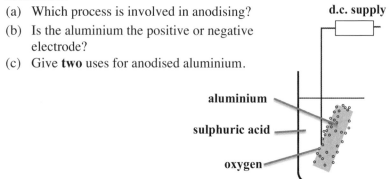

aluminium

sulphuric acid

oxygen

d.c. supply

Corrosion

1. Each year corrosion costs our country millions of pounds.
    (a) Explain what is meant by corrosion.
    (b) What special term is applied to the corrosion of iron?
    (c) Consider this list of substances:

    *glass,   magnesium,   sandstone,   sulphur,   calcium carbonate,
    sodium,   aluminium,   plastic,   calcium,   zinc*

    Copy the table and place each of the substances in the appropriate column.

A substance that corrodes	A substance that does NOT corrode

2. (a) Apart from iron, what **two** substances are necessary for rusting to occur?
    (b) When iron rusts, what happens to the iron atoms?

3. Explain each of the following.
    (a) Steel for kitchen dish-racks is sometimes coated with plastic to prevent corrosion.
    (b) A ship with a steel hull corrodes faster at sea than on a freshwater loch.
    (c) Painted iron railings corrode less rapidly than unpainted railings.
    (d) A steel motor car body is connected to the negative terminal of the car battery to reduce corrosion.

4. Acid rain is common in industrial areas.

    (a) In what way does acid rain affect the rate of corrosion of metals?

    (b) Explain your answer.

5. Three test tubes were set up as shown.

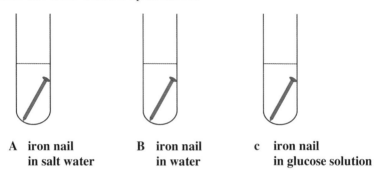

| **A** iron nail | **B** iron nail | **c** iron nail |
| in salt water | in water | in glucose solution |

Ferroxyl indicator was added to each of the tubes. On inspection it was found that the nail in tube **A** had corroded most. The amount of corrosion in tubes **B** and **C** was much the same.

    (a) In what way does ferroxyl indicator help to compare the rates of corrosion?

    (b) Salt in the water speeds up the rate of corrosion but glucose does not. What does this indicate about the bonding in glucose?

6. The experiment shown was carried out to investigate the rusting of iron.

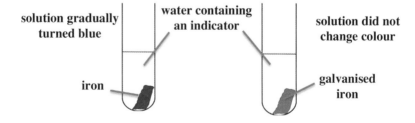

solution gradually turned blue

water containing an indicator

solution did not change colour

iron

galvanised iron

    (a) Give the name of the indicator used.

    (b) What is meant by galvanised iron?

7. Both silver and gold are used to cover objects made of steel. As well as providing an attractive finish, the steel is protected against corrosion.

    (a) What name is given to the process of coating steel with silver or gold?

    (b) Explain why the coating protects the iron against corrosion.

8. Equipment used by Scott in his final expedition to the South Pole in 1912 has been found recently. It shows very little sign of rusting.

    Explain why iron rusts so slowly when the temperature is well below 0 °C.

9. Oil rigs, made of iron and steel, corrode readily at sea.

    State **one** method which could be used to help prevent corrosion of oil rigs and explain briefly how the method works.

10. 'Tin' cans are made of iron that has been coated with tin. Three cans were left outside to investigate the corrosion of the cans.

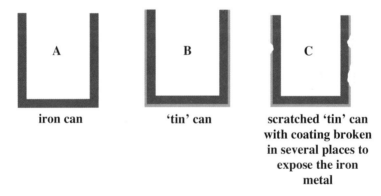

<table>
<tr><td align="center">**A**</td><td align="center">**B**</td><td align="center">**C**</td></tr>
<tr><td align="center">**iron can**</td><td align="center">**'tin' can**</td><td align="center">**scratched 'tin' can with coating broken in several places to expose the iron metal**</td></tr>
</table>

    (a) (i) In which experiment will the iron **not** rust?
         (ii) Explain your answer.
    (b) (i) In which experiment will the iron rust fastest?
         (ii) Explain your answer.

11. Two corrosion experiments with iron nails are shown.

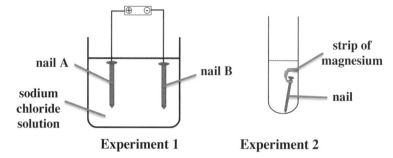

Experiment 1   Experiment 2

(a) In experiment 1, which nail, **A** or **B**, will be protected against rusting?
(b) In experiment 2, why does the magnesium protect the nail from rusting?
(c) For each of these experiments describe how the method is actually used to protect iron or steel in an everyday situation.

12. **X** and **Y** are two metals. When each is attached to iron only **Y** decreases the speed of rusting of iron.

(a) Which metal is more reactive, **X** or **Y**?
(b) Which metal would be most effective in sacrificially protecting iron?

13. A student set up the following experiment.

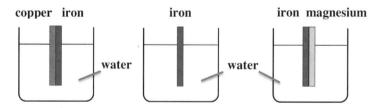

(a) Identify the experiment in which the corrosion of iron will be
    (i) fastest,
    (ii) greatly reduced.
(b) Explain each of your answers.

14. Chromium-plated steel rusts quickly if scratched.

    (a) What does this tell you about the reactivity of chromium?

    (b) Name another metal that would increase the speed of corrosion of steel in a similar way.

15. Dustbins used to be made from iron that had been dipped into molten zinc.

    (a) Name the process that takes place when iron is coated with zinc.

    (b) Explain why zinc was preferred to tin for protecting dustbins.

16. Dental amalgam is a mixture of metals including mercury, silver and tin. The amalgam slowly corrodes in the mouth. Corrosion is more rapid if the amalgam makes contact with a gold filling in a neighbouring tooth.

    Explain why contact with gold increases the rate of corrosion of the dental amalgam.

17. Archaeologists found some corroded silver coins and a badly rusted sword.

    (a) The silver coins were partly restored by wrapping them in zinc foil in a beaker of salt solution.

    Explain the reactions taking place.

    (b) The iron blade was attached to its handle by a copper band.

    Explain why, although the copper was uncorroded, the iron had rusted badly.

18. Ethylene glycol is used as an antifreeze in car radiators.

    ethylene glycol
    $$\begin{array}{c} CH_2-CH_2 \\ |\quad\;\; | \\ OH\quad OH \end{array}$$

    Salt could also act as an antifreeze but would cause rusting in the radiator. Why does ethylene glycol **not** cause rusting?

19. *"OLD COPPER BOTTOM"*

"Old Copper Bottom" was the nickname of William Forbes of Stirling who lived during the 18th century.

Forbes made his fortune by buying up all the available copper in the country when he heard rumours that the Navy was planning to experiment with copper sheeting on the hulls of its wooden warships. He sold the copper to the Navy at a large profit and when the experiment failed because of the use of iron nails, he bought the copper back at a lower price.

Forbes then pointed out the obvious fact the the copper nails should have been used. After this he was able to resell the copper to the Navy and made a second large profit.

Explain why it is 'obvious' that copper and not iron nails should have been used in the experiment.

20. Corrosion involves atoms at the surface of a metal losing electrons and changing to metal ions.

(a) State the name of this kind of reaction.

(b) Write ion-electron equations to show what happens to the metal atoms during the corrosion of

    (i) iron,   (ii) zinc,

    (iii) magnesium,   (iv) aluminium.

(c) During corrosion, iron(II) ions form iron(III) ions.

    (i) Write the ion-electron equation for this reaction.

    (ii) Is this an example of oxidation or reduction?

(d) Write the ion-electron equation to show how hydroxide ions are formed during corrosion of a metal.

21. Acid mists lead to faster corrosion of iron.

    (a) (i)   Write ion-electron equations for each of the **two** reactions that occur when iron is corroded by acid.

         (ii) State whether each reaction is an example of oxidation or reduction.

    (b) Why does galvanising **not** protect iron permanently from corrosion by acid?

22. In the 19th century, Humphrey Davy suggested that the Royal Navy could protect the copper sheeting on the hulls of its ships from corrosion by attaching small patches of iron to them.

    (a) (i)   Write the ion-electron equation to show what happens to the atoms when copper corrodes.

         (ii) Is this an example of oxidation or reduction?

    (b) Explain why attaching patches of iron would have prevented the copper from corroding.

23. When iron rusts, metal atoms change to metal ions.

$$Fe (s) \rightarrow Fe^{2+} (aq) + 2e^- \quad \textbf{oxidation}$$

Water and oxygen are required for corrosion to take place. The electrons lost by the metal atoms are accepted by the water and oxygen.

$$2H_2O (l) + O_2 (g) + 4e^- \rightarrow 4OH^- (aq) \ \textbf{reduction}$$

Ferroxyl indicator is a solution that will react with both the oxidation product of rusting, iron(II) ions, Fe^{2+} (aq), and the reduction product of corrosion, hydroxide ions, OH^- (aq).
A colour change is associated with each of the reactions.

Reaction	Product	Colour observed
oxidation (of iron)	Fe^{2+} (aq) ions	blue
reduction	OH^- (aq) ions	pink

Consider the following cells.

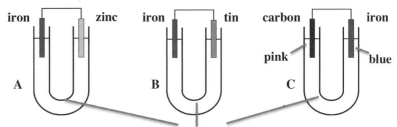

gel containing ferroxyl indicator plus an electrolyte

(a) In cell **C** (i) state the direction of electron flow,

             (ii) write the ion-electron equation for the reaction at each electrode.

(b) In cell **B** (i) state the direction of electron flow,

             (ii) give the colour, if any, that will be observed at each electrode,

             (iii) write the ion-electron equation for the reaction at each electrode.

(b) In cell **A** (i) state the direction of electron flow,

             (ii) give the colour, if any, that will be observed at each electrode,

             (iii) write the ion-electron equation for the reaction at each electrode.

Plastics

1.* Plastics are synthetic materials that have been used to replace natural materials.

    (a) What is meant by a synthetic material?

    (b) (i) State **three** properties that are common to most plastics.

        (ii) Give **three** examples that show how the use of a plastic is related to its properties.

    (c) Give an example of where (in and around the house) a plastic has been use to replace

        (i) wood,

        (ii) metal,

        (iii) paper.

2.* Thermosetting plastics have different properties from thermoplastics.

    (a) Explain what is meant by

        (i) a thermosetting plastic,

        (ii) a thermoplastic.

    (b) Give **two** examples of each.

3.* A plastic bottle has the following label.

> **NON-BIODEGRADABLE**
> **To dispose of this plastic bottle,**
> **simply fill with hot water.**
> **When soft, empty and flatten.**
> **DO NOT BURN.**

    (a) Explain what is meant by non-biodegradable.

    (b) What type of plastic is suggested by the instructions on the label?

    (c) What problems can arise from burning plastics?

4. Plastics are examples of polymers. Different monomers are used to make different plastics.
   (a) Explain what is meant by
       (i)   a monomer,
       (ii) a polymer.
   (b) Name the process that takes place when a polymer is made from a monomer.
   (c) Name the polymer that is made from
       (i)   phenylethene (styrene),
       (ii) propene,
       (iii) chloroethene (vinyl chloride).
   (d) What is common to the structures of all of the monomers that are given in part (c) above?

5. Poly(ethene) is a widely used polymer.
   (a) (i)   Name the monomer unit.
       (ii) Draw the full structural formula for the monomer unit.
   (b) Draw the structure of part of a poly(ethene) chain to show how **three** monomer units have joined together.

6.
```
    H   H
    |   |
    C = C        acrylonitrile
    |   |
    H   CN
```
   (a) Name the polymer made from acrylonitrile.
   (b) Draw the structure of part of the polymer chain to show how **three** monomer units have joined together.

7. PTFE is an addition polymer made from tetrafluoroethene.
   (a) What does PTFE stand for?
   (b) Draw the full structural formula for tetrafluoroethene.
   (c) Draw the structure of part of a PTFE chain to show how **three** monomer units have joined together.

8. Poly(propene) is used to make many kitchen items.

    (a) (i) Name the monomer unit.

    (ii) Draw the full structural formula for the monomer unit.

    (b) Draw the structure of part of a poly(propene) chain to show how **three** monomer units have joined together.

9. Perspex is used to make safety screens, spectacle lenses and aeroplane windows. The following diagram shows part of a molecule of perspex.

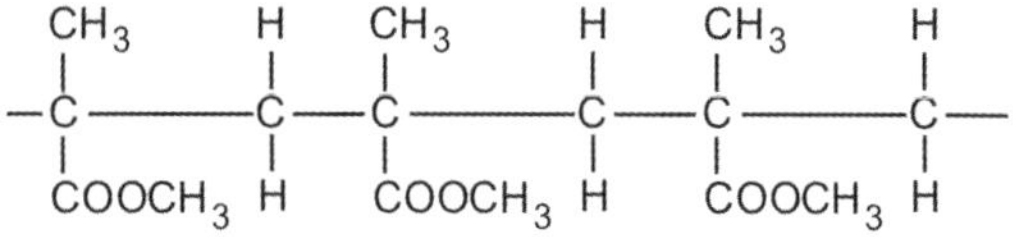

    (a) Draw the structural formula for the repeating unit in perspex.

    (b) Draw the structural formula for the monomer used to make perspex.

    (c) What type of polymerisation takes place when perspex is produced from the monomer?

10. Orlon is a synthetic fibre made from monomers with the following structure.

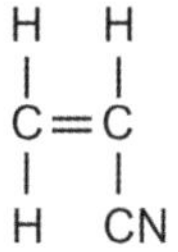

    (a) Draw the structural formula for the repeating unit in Orlon.

    (b) Draw the structure of part of an Orlon chain to show how **three** monomer units have joined together.

11. Polyvinylidene chloride is an addition polymer.
Part of the polymer chain is shown.

```
     H   Cl  H   Cl  H   Cl
     |   |   |   |   |   |
  —C — C — C — C — C — C—
     |   |   |   |   |   |
     H   Cl  H   Cl  H   Cl
```

(a) What is meant by an addition polymer?
(b) Name the monomer used to make polyvinylidene chloride.
(c) How many repeating units are shown?
(d) Draw the full structural formula for the vinylidene chloride monomer.

12. Poly(butene) is used to make pipes that carry hot water under pressure. This is very useful in plumbing and underfloor heatlng.

Poly(butene) is made using the following monomer.

```
     H   H   H   H
     |   |   |   |
     C = C — C — C — H
     |       |   |
     H       H   H
```

(a) Draw the structure of part of the poly(butene) chain to show how **three** monomer units have joined together.
(b) The butene monomer shown has a number of isomers.
    Draw the structure of an isomer that
    (i) could also be used to form a polymer,
    (ii) could **not** be used to form a polymer.

13. Polymers can be classified depending on how the monomers join together.
(a) Explain the difference between an addition and a condensation polymer.
(b) Name each of the **two** groups that are involved in the condensation reaction to form a polyester.

14. Terylene is a common polyester.

The structure of terylene is shown.

where ■ and □ represent the carbon structure in each of the monomer molecules.

(a) Is Terylene an addition or a condensation polymer?

(b) Draw a structure to represent each of the **two** monomers.

15. Polylactic acid is a biopolymer that can be made from lactic acid.

(a) Draw the structure of part of the polylactic acid chain to show how **three** monomer units have joined together.

(b) Name this type of polymerisation.

Fertilisers

1*. The flow chart shows part of the nitrogen cycle.

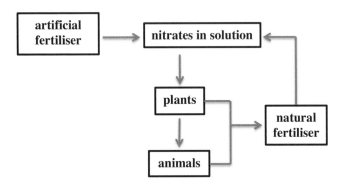

(a) Explain what is meant by
    (i)   an artificial fertiliser,
    (ii)   a natural fertiliser.
(b) Give an example of each.
(c) Why is it often necessary to add artificial fertiliser to the cycle?
(d) Give **one** example of an environmental problem that can be caused by the use of artificial fertiliser.

2*. Fertilisers are compounds that restore to the soil the essential elements for plant growth. They must also have a particular property.

(a) Name the **three** main elements that are restored to the soil through use of fertiliser.
(b) What is the particular property that fertilisers must have?
(c) Explain why woodland growth does **not** require the use of fertiliser while farmland requires the use of large quantities of fertiliser.

3*. The graph shows how the
   level of nitrates in the soil
   of a farmer's field varied
   throughout a particular year.

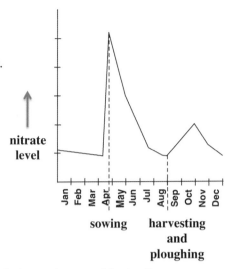

(a) Suggest why the level of nitrates increased in April.

(b) Suggest why the level of nitrates decreased from April to August.

(c) Nitrates are very soluble in water and this allows essential
   elements to be taken in by the roots of crop plants very quickly.

   Suggest why the solubility of nitrates can also be a disadvantage in
   their use as fertilisers.

4*. Information about two fertilisers is given in the following table.

Name	Solubility in water
ammonium phosphate	dissolves easily
urea	dissolves slowly

Ammonium phosphate contains two elements that are essential for
plant growth.

(a) (i) Name an element **not** found in ammonium phosphate that plants
   require in large amounts.

   (ii) Name a compound that gardeners could use to supply this
   element.

(b) Suggest why urea is particularly suitable as a fertiliser in very
   wet countries.

5. Ammonium nitrate fertiliser can be made by the NITRAM Process as shown.

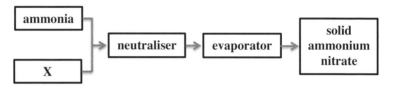

(a) Write the formula for ammonia and ammonium nitrate.
(b) Name **X**.

6. Nitrate fertilisers are made from nitric acid.

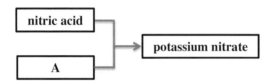

(a) Name reagent **A**.
(b) Name the other product of this reaction.
(c) State **two** reasons why nitrate compounds are useful fertilisers.

7. Compound **X**, formula $(NH_4)_2SO_4$, is made from ammonia.
(a) Name compound **X**.
(b) Name the chemical that reacts with ammonia to form compound **X**.

8. At the turn of the century a team of scientists led by Fritz Haber discovered a cheap way to make an important compound for the fertiliser industry. This is now called the Haber Process.

(a) Name the compound that Haber produced.
(b) Which catalyst is used for the reaction?
(c) State **two** other conditions that are necessary for a successful yield of the compound.

9. The diagram shows how ammonia is made industrially.

(a) Give a use for ammonia.
(b) Name gas **A** and gas **B**.
(c) Name industrial process **X**.
(d) How is ammonia removed from the reaction mixture?

10. The data below refers to the formation of ammonia by the Haber process.

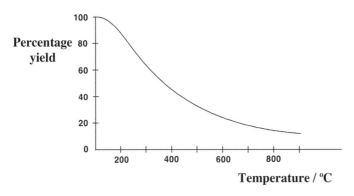

(a) Name the elements that are necessary for the manufacture of ammonia.
(b) From the information given above, what happens to the yield as the temperature is increased?
(c) Explain why the reaction is carried out at a moderately high temperature.
(d) Explain why the yield of ammonia is not 100%.

11. Ammonia is manufactured in industry by the Haber Process. In this process, the percentage yield of ammonia varies with pressure.

The graph shows the percentage yield against pressure, at 350 °C.

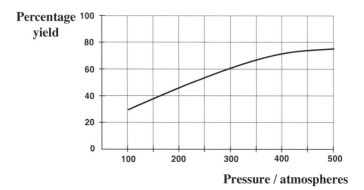

Pressure / atmospheres

(a) Copy the graph and add a second curve to show how the percentage yield would vary with pressure at a higher temperature.

(b) Why is this reaction carried out at 350 °C and **not** at 450 °C?

12. In the manufacture of ammonia by the Haber Process, the reactant gases are compressed from a pressure of 25 atmospheres to 200 atmospheres. This raises the temperature so the mixture of gases is cooled before it enters the catalytic converter.

(a) Suggest why the temperature of the gases is lowered before entering the catalytic converter.

(b) Suggest why the pipes used in this industrial process have thick walls.

13. The flow diagram below outlines some of the stages in the industrial manufacture of nitric acid.

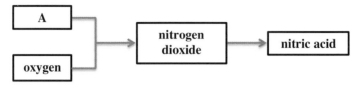

(a) Why is nitrogen dioxide **not** made from nitrogen?

(b) Name gas **A**.

(c) Explain why the reaction in the catalyst chamber is carried out at a moderately high temperature.

(d) (i) Is it necessary to continue heating the catalyst chamber throughout the process?

(ii) Explain your answer.

14. The flow chart refers to an industrial chemical complex.

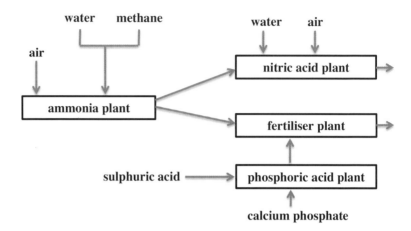

(a) Give **two** reasons why air and water are used as raw materials in the ammonia plant.

(b) Which reactant for the ammonia plant is produced in the reaction between methane and water?

(c) The nitric acid is produced when nitrogen dioxide dissolves in water.
   (i) Name the industrial process that converts ammonia into nitrogen dioxide.
   (ii) Name the catalyst used.

(d) Write the formula for calcium phosphate.

(e) Name the salt formed in the fertiliser plant.

Percentage mass

1. Calculate the percentage (by mass) of each of the elements present in the following compounds.

    (a) CO_2 (b) CH_4
    (e) NH_3 (d) $CuSO_4$
    (e) $CaCO_3$ (f) K_2SO_4
    (g) $Al(OH)_3$ (h) $Mg(NO_3)_2$

2. Urea, $CO(NH_2)_2$, ammonium sulphate, $(NH_4)_2SO_4$ and ammonium nitrate, NH_4NO_3, are three fertilisers that supply nitrogen.

    Find the most useful fertiliser by calculating which has the highest percentage mass of nitrogen.

3. Ammonium phosphate, $(NH_4)_3PO_4$, is a synthetic fertiliser.

    (a) Calculate the mass of nitrogen in 100 g of ammonium phosphate.
    (b) Calculate the mass of phosphorus in 1 kg of the fertiliser.

Radioactivity

1. Nuclear fusion takes place in the stars.
    (a) What is meant by nuclear fusion?
    (b) Why is it important?

2. The radiation that is all around is known as background radiation.
    Give a source of
    (a) artificial radiation,
    (b) natural radiation.

3. The nuclei of radioisotopes are unstable.
    (a) What is the cause of this instability?
    (b) What happens in the nucleus that results in a stable isotope?

4. $^2_1 H$ + $^2_1 H$ ➜ $^3_2 He$ + $^1_0 n$

    (a) Name this type of reaction.
    (b) Where do reactions of this type occur naturally?

5. Copy and complete the following table.

Radiation	Alpha	Beta	Gamma
Symbol			
Mass			
Charge			

6. Alpha, beta and gamma radiation have different penetrating properties.
    Name the type of radiation that is
    (a) able to penetrate 5 cm of lead,
    (b) stopped by a sheet of paper,
    (c) stopped by a sheet of aluminium.

7. The following experiment was carried out using a radioisotope that
    emitted alpha, beta and gamma radiation.

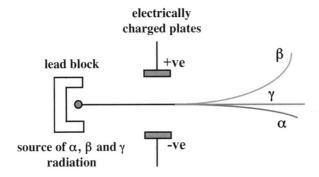

    (a) Why is the radioisotope surrounded by a thick lead block?
    (b) Explain the paths taken by the **three** different types of radiation.

Nuclear equations

1. $$^{225}_{88}\text{Ra} \rightarrow ^{225}_{89}\text{Ac} + \text{y}$$

    $$^{217}_{85}\text{At} \rightarrow ^{213}_{83}\text{Bi} + \text{z}$$

    State the mass and charge of each of the particles **y** and **z**, and identify them.

2. Identify the isotope that is formed when
    (a) sodium-24 emits beta particles,
    (b) plutonium-242 emits alpha particles.

3. Write a nuclear equation for
    (a) α-decay of $^{210}_{84}\text{Po}$,
    (b) β-decay of tritium $^{3}_{1}\text{H}$,
    (c) α-decay of $^{226}_{88}\text{Ra}$,
    (d) β-decay of $^{90}_{38}\text{Sr}$.

4. (a) Write a nuclear equation to show what happens when ^{232}Th undergoes α-emission.
    (b) Show, by calculation, that the neutron to proton ratio has increased.

5. $^{27}_{13}\text{Al}$ can absorb an alpha particle with the emission of a neutron, forming a product **Y**.

    Write a nuclear equation to illustrate this reaction and identify **Y**.

6. Complete each of the following nuclear equations and identify **R** and **S**.

   (a) $^{6}_{3}\text{Li}$ $+$ $^{1}_{0}\text{n}$ $\rightarrow$ $^{3}_{1}\text{H}$ $+$ **R**

   (b) $^{238}_{92}\text{U}$ $+$ $^{4}_{2}\text{He}$ $\rightarrow$ $^{239}_{94}\text{Pu}$ $+$ 3**S**

7. State the mass and charge of each of the particles **x** and **y**, and identify them.

   (a) $^{14}_{7}\text{N}$ $+$ $^{4}_{2}\text{He}$ $\rightarrow$ $^{17}_{8}\text{O}$ $+$ **x**

   (b) $^{6}_{3}\text{Li}$ $+$ **y** $\rightarrow$ $^{3}_{1}\text{H}$ $+$ $^{4}_{2}\text{He}$

8. (a) $^{10}_{5}\text{B}$ $+$ $^{1}_{0}\text{n}$ $\rightarrow$ $^{p}_{q}\text{X}$ $+$ $^{4}_{2}\text{He}$

   Write values for **p** and **q** and identify element **X**.

   (b) $^{a}_{b}\text{Y}$ $+$ $^{1}_{0}\text{n}$ $\rightarrow$ $^{24}_{11}\text{Na}$

   Write values for **a** and **b** and identify element **Y**.

9. What is the source of ^{206}Pb, if it is formed by β-emission, followed by α-emission?

10. **P** is a radioisotope which undergoes transitions as follows.

β-emission		β-emission		α-emission	
P	$\rightarrow$	**Q**	$\rightarrow$	**R**	$\rightarrow$ **S**

    If the atomic number of **P** is 88, and its mass number is 228, what is the atomic number and mass number for isotope **S**?

11. Plutonium-242 is a radioactive isotope that decays to form a stable isotope $^{b}_{a}\text{X}$ by the following sequence of emissions.

    α, α, β, β, α

    Write values for **a** and **b** and identify element **X**.

Half-life

1. For each of the following pairs, state whether or not both species have the same half-life.

    (a) 1 g ^{212}Pb and l00 g ^{212}Pb

    (b) 1 g ^{212}Pb and 1 g ^{212}Pb^{2+}

    (c) 1 mol ^{210}Pb and 1 mol ^{212}Pb

    (d) 1 mol ^{210}Pb and 1 mol ^{212}PbO

    (e) 1 mol of solid ^{210}Pb and 1 mol of molten ^{210}Pb

2. Samples of radium oxide and radium sulphate both contain the same radioisotope.

    Why does a 1 g sample of the oxide show a different intensity of radiation from the sulphate?

3. ^{24}Na is a radioactive isotope of sodium with a half-life of 15 hours. A sample of ^{24}Na has a mass of 200 g.

    (a) What is meant by half-life?

    (b) What will be the remaining mass of the original sample after 120 hours?

4. Polonium-218 is an alpha emitting radioisotope.
    After 6 minutes the mass of the radioisotope was found to be one eighth of the original.

    What is the half-life of the radioisotope?

5. The initial radioactivity from a sample of actinium chloride is 120 counts/minute.

    If the half-life of actinium is 6 hours, how long will it take for the sample of the chloride to reach a reading of 15 counts/minute?

6. The rate of alpha emission from a 48 day old sample of a radioactive isotope was found to be a quarter of that of the original sample.

   What is the half-life of the sample?

7. A radioisotope used in a hospital has a half-life of 1.5 hours. It has a count rate of 8000 counts min^{-1} at 9.00 a.m.

   (a) What would the count rate be at 1.30 p.m. on the same day?

   (b) An aqueous solution of a compound containing the radioisotope was prepared.
   What effect would this have on the half-life?

8. $^{210}_{84}$Po, which has a half-life of 140 days, decays by α-emission to give a stable isotope.

   What fraction of the sample will remain unchanged after 280 days?

9. After 15 days a sample contained 0.1 g of radioactive bismuth, half-life 5 days.

   What was the mass of the original sample?

10. The isotope of iodine-131 is radioactive and is manufactured for medicinal use.

    If, 24 days after manufacture, only 32.75 g of an original one mole sample of radioactive iodine remains, calculate the half-life of the isotope.

11. The radioactive isotope $^{210}_{84}$Po decays to $^{206}_{82}$Pb, which is stable.

    Calculate the mass of lead that would be formed from 1 mol of $^{210}_{84}$Po after two half-lives.

12. A radioisotope **X** decays to give a stable product. The decay curve is shown.

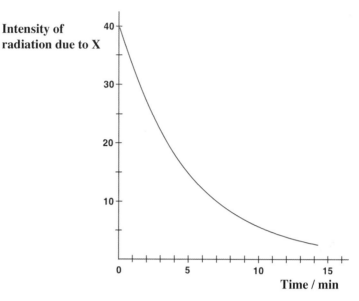

(a) What is the half-life of isotope **X**?

(b) The half-life of a radioisotope **Y** is 6 min.

Copy the graph (no graph paper required), and add a dotted line to show the decay curve for isotope **Y**, assuming that it starts at the same intensity of radiation as isotope **X**.

13. The half-life of a radioisotope is 8 hours.

(a) Draw a graph (no graph paper required) to show the variation with time of the intensity of radiation due to the decay of a 10 g sample that has an intensity of 40 counts/minute.

(b) Using the same scale and axes, add a dotted line to show what the graph would be for a 5 g sample.

14. An 8 g sample of $^{24}_{11}$Na undergoes β-decay to form $^{24}_{12}$Mg as shown in the graph below.

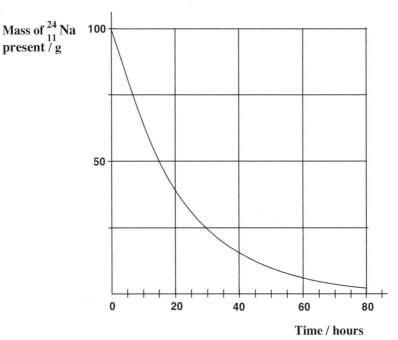

Mass of $^{24}_{11}$Na present / g

(a) From the graph, what is the half-life of $^{24}_{11}$Na?

(b) What mass of product would be formed from the sample after 45 hours?

15. The decay curve for the radioisotope tritium, $^{3}_{1}$H, is shown below.

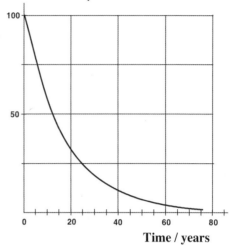

Intensity of radiation / %

Time / years

(a) (i) From the graph, what is the half-life of tritium?
    (ii) Calculate the time taken for the radioactivity to fall to ⅛th of its original value.

(b) If the temperature of the tritium sample is increased, how would this affect its rate of decay?

16. The radio-isotope $^{131}_{53}$I is used in hospitals. It has a half-life of 8 days and decays to give a stable product.

A bag of hospital linen contaminated with iodine $^{131}_{53}$I was found to give a count rate of 320 counts s^{-1}.

(a) Using graph paper, draw a graph to show how the count rate of the linen will change with time.

(b) Hospitals are not allowed to dispose of material contaminated with $^{131}_{53}$I until the count rate has fallen to 30 counts s^{-1}.
    Use your graph to determine how long the bag of linen must be stored before disposal.

Chemical analysis

1. What is the difference between qualitative and quantitative analysis?

2. Flame tests can be used to identify the presence of particular metals in solutions of metal ions.
   (a) What is the characteristic flame colour of each of the following metal ions?
       (i) copper
       (ii) potassium
       (iii) sodium
   (b) Is a flame test an example of qualitative or quantitative analysis?

3. Litmus paper turns red in acid and blue in alkali.
   (a) Why is the use of litmus paper an example of qualitative analysis?
   (b) Why is pH measurement an example of quantitative analysis?

4. A sample of water is taken from a factory effluent.
   What is the concentration of H^+ (aq) ions in the water if 25 cm^3 of sodium hydroxide solution (concentration 0.002 mol l^{-1}) is neutralised by 34.5 cm^3 of the sample?

5. When silver nitrate solution is added to 25 cm^3 of a water sample containing chloride ions, 2.87 g of silver chloride is formed.

   $$Ag^+ (aq) \quad + \quad Cl^- (aq) \quad \rightarrow \quad AgCl (s)$$

   (a) (i) Calculate the number of moles of silver chloride that is formed.
       (ii) Calculate the concentration of chloride ions in the sample.
   (b) Is this an example of qualitative or quantitative analysis?

Graphs

1. When copper(II) sulphate solution is placed in a beam of light, some light is absorbed and some passes through.
   The results of an investigation are shown below.

Concentration of CuSO$_4$/moles per litre	0.05	0.2	0.4	0.6	0.8	1.0
Light passing through / %	74.0	29.0	11.0	5.0	3.0	2.0

   (a) Draw a **line graph** to show these results.
   (b) State the relationship between the amount of light passing through and the concentration of the copper(II) sulphate solution.
   (c) Use your graph to estimate the concentration of a copper(II) sulphate solution that allows 50% of the light to pass through.

2. A student added lumps of zinc to dilute sulphuric acid. The mass of the flask and contents were noted every two minutes.

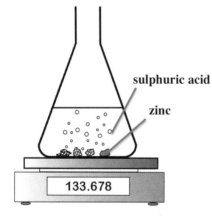

Time / min	Total mass loss / mg
0	0
2	130
4	210
6	260
8	300
10	330
12	330

sulphuric acid

zinc

133.678

   (a) Why was there a loss of mass from the flask?
   (b) Draw a **line graph** of loss of mass against time.
   (c) Use your graph to find the total mass loss after 2.5 min.

3. Sea water contains dissolved oxygen

    The table shows the relationship between the temperature of the water and the amount of dissolved oxygen.

Temperature of water / °C	0	20	40	60	70	80
Concentration of dissolved oxygen / grams in each cubic metre	69.4	43.4	30.8	22.7	18.6	13.8

(a) Draw a **line graph** to show these results.

(b) The average temperature of the seas around Scotland is approximately 9 °C.

    Use your graph to find the concentration of oxygen available at this temperature.

(c) Use your graph to find the temperature of the water that contains 25 g of dissolved oxygen in each cubic metre.

4. The alkanes are a family of hydrocarbons each with a different number of carbon atoms per molecule.

    The table shows the boiling points for each of the first five members.

Alkane	Number of carbon atoms per molecule	Boiling point / °C
A	1	-162
B	2	-89
C	3	-42
D	4	-1
E	5	36

(a) Draw a **bar graph** to show this information.

(b) Identify the alkanes shown in the table that are gases at

    (i)   -50 °C,

    (ii) 10 °C.

5. The alkynes are a family of hydrocarbons each with a different number of carbon atoms per molecule.

The table shows the formula mass for each of the first five members.

Number of carbon atoms per molecule	Formula mass
2	26
3	40
4	54
5	68
6	82

(a) Draw a **bar graph** to show this information.

(b) Using either the information in the table or your bar graph, state the formula mass of the alkyne with 8 carbon atoms per molecule.

Skills

1. Nuclear reactors can overheat and become very dangerous.
   Liquid sodium can be used to cool down reactors. It flows round the reactor in pipes.

   Suggest why sodium is used rather than iron.
   You may wish to use page 5 of the Data Booklet to help you.

2. Lawn sand contains ammonium sulphate and iron(II) sulphate.
   One compound improves grass growth, the other is present to kill moss.

   Name the ion that is present in lawn sand to kill moss.

3. This graph shows how much lime a gardener needs to add to produce a soil of the desired pH, e.g. if the soil had a pH of 4, but a pH of 7 was required, 1.3 kg of lime would be needed for every 10 m^2 of soil.

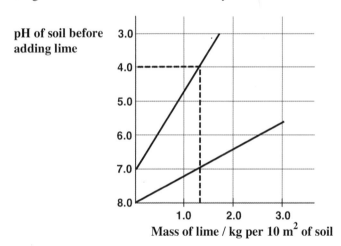

Find the mass of lime that is needed to increase the pH of soil
(a) from pH 6 to pH 7 in a 10 m^2 garden,
(b) from pH 7 to pH 8 in a 10 m^2 garden,
(c) from pH 6 to pH 8 in a 100 m^2 garden.

4. The concentration of sodium hypochlorite, NaOCl (aq), in a bleach can be found by adding an excess of dilute hydrochloric acid to a measured sample of the bleach. The acid reacts with the sodium hypochlorite and the volume of chlorine given off is measured.

$$NaOCl\,(aq) \quad + \quad 2HCl\,(aq) \quad \rightarrow \quad NaCl\,(aq) \quad + \quad H_2O\,(l) \quad + \quad Cl_2\,(g)$$

In an investigation of three different household bleaches, the following results were obtained.

Bleach	Volume of bleach used /cm^3	Volume of chlorine produced / cm^3
A	6	100
B	9	150
C	4	90

Find, **by calculation**, which bleach contains most sodium hypochlorite per litre.

5. Refer to page 8 of the Data Booklet.

For each of the compounds shown, decide if 5 g will dissolve in 1 litre of water at room temperature.
Use one of the following letters for your answer.
   X All the solid will dissolve.
   Y Some of the solid will **not** dissolve.
   Z Not enough information is given to decide.
(a) calcium oxide
(b) lead(II) iodide
(c) potassium chloride

6. The uses of metals are related to their properties.

Metal	Density (g /cm^3)	Relative strength	Relative electrical conductivity
Aluminium	2.7	1.0	3.8
Steel	7.9	4.0	1.0
Copper	8.9	2.5	5.9

Overhead electricity cables have a steel core surrounded by an aluminium sheath.

aluminium sheath
steel core

Using information from the table, suggest
(a) an advantage of using aluminum rather than copper for the cable,
(b) why the cables have a steel core.

7. An electric current was passed through different solutions.
   The results are shown in the table.

Solution	Positive electrode product	Negative electrode product
hydrochloric acid	chlorine	hydrogen
potassium chloride	chlorine	hydrogen
sulphuric acid	oxygen	hydrogen
sodium nitrate	oxygen	hydrogen
nitric acid	oxygen	hydrogen
silver nitrate	oxygen	silver
potassium sulphate	oxygen	hydrogen

(a) From the results, suggest a general statement that can be made about acids.
(b) From the results, predict the product at the positive and negative electrodes when each of the following solutions is used used.
   (i) sodium chloride
   (ii) potassium nitrate

8. The percentage of oxygen in the air can be determined by passing air is over heated copper.

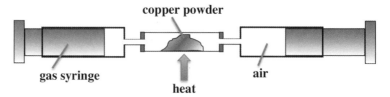

The copper powder reacts with the oxygen of the air to form copper(II) oxide.

A student obtained the following results.

Volume of air at start of experiment = 80 cm^3

Volume of gas at end of experiment = 64.4 cm^3

(a) Suggest a reason why the air is passed backwards and forwards over the heated copper.

(b) Calculate the percentage of oxygen in the sample of air.

(c) In a second experiment using fresh copper, the percentage of oxygen in the sample of air was found to be lower.

Suggest a reason for this result.

9. The ability of different substances to conduct electricity when dissolved in water was investigated by a student.

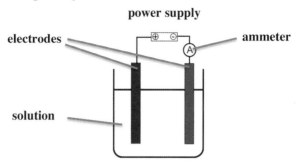

Here are the results.

Substance	Concentration of solution / mol l^{-1}	Current /mA
sodium chloride	0.005	21
sodium chloride	0.002	11
sodium chloride	0.001	7
hydrochloric acid	0.005	62
hydrochloric acid	0.002	27
hydrochloric acid	0.001	20
sodium hydroxide	0.005	32
sodium hydroxide	0.002	15
sodium hydroxide	0.001	11

(a) Identify **two** variables that must be kept constant to make the investigation fair.

(b) From the results, state the effect of changing concentration on the ability of a substance to conduct electricity when dissolved in water.

(c) Arrange the three substances in order of their ability to conduct electricity when dissolved in water. (Put the best conductor first.)

10. White phosphorus readily catches fire in air.
    The following diagrams show this reaction.

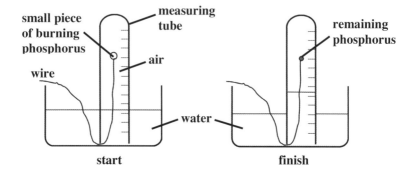

start   finish

(a) What would have been the effect on the final water level inside the
    tube, if a larger piece of phosphorus had been used?

(b) Explain your answer.

11. Water can exist in three different states: solid, liquid and gas.
    The state depends on temperature and pressure.
    The diagram below shows these relationships.

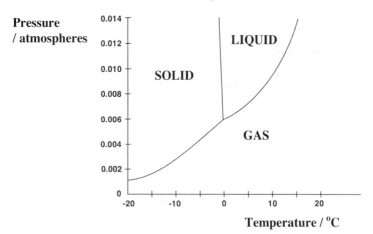

(a) In which state would water exist at 15 °C and 0.007 atmospheres?

(b) Solid water at 0.004 atmospheres is allowed to warm up.
    The pressure is kept constant.
    At what temperature would the solid water change into a gas?

Design and plan

1. Hydrogen is less dense than air.

    Identify the most suitable arrangement for collecting a sample of
    hydrogen.

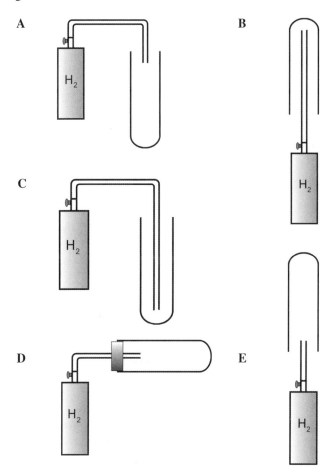

A

B

C

D

E

H_2

2. Carbon monoxide gas can be bubbled through water to monitor the flow rate, then passed through lumps of calcium chloride to dry the gas.

Using a test tube and a U-tube draw a labelled diagram to show the arrangement you would use to do this.

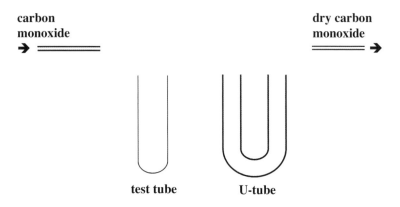

carbon monoxide ➔ ═══

dry carbon monoxide ═══ ➔

test tube   **U-tube**

3. Vegetable oils can be given an "iodine value". This is the volume of iodine solution that is decolourised by 10 cm^3 of oil.

You are given the following apparatus.

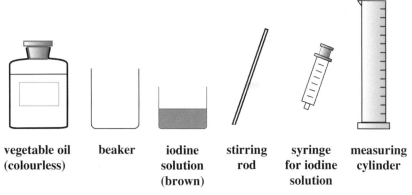

vegetable oil (colourless)   **beaker**   **iodine solution (brown)**   **stirring rod**   **syringe for iodine solution**   **measuring cylinder**

Describe how you would use this apparatus to find the iodine value of the oil.

4. Chlorine can be prepared in the laboratory by the reaction of **concentrated hydrochloric acid** with **manganese(IV) oxide**.

(a) Using the equipment given below, draw a labelled diagram to show how chlorine gas can be generated.

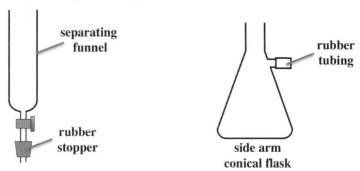

(b) The chlorine gas is bubbled through a test tube of water to remove the acid fumes. It is then bubbled through concentrated sulphuric acid in a second test tube to dry the gas. The dried chlorine gas gas is collected in a gas jar.

Starting with the rubber tubing from the chlorine generator, draw a labelled diagram to show how the sample of dry gas would be collected.

Chlorine is more dense than air.

5.

> ### Workcard - carbon dioxide
>
> 1. Put some powdered chalk in a test tube.
> 2. Clamp the mouth of a test tube in clamp stand at an angle of approximately 45 $^{\circ}$.
> 3. Fit a delivery tube to the test tube.
> 4. Put 10 cm^3 of water into a second test tube and add a few drops of Universal indicator solution.
> 5. Place the end of the delivery tube into the indicator.
> 6. Heat the chalk with the bunsen burner.

(a) Draw a labelled diagram of the apparatus for the experiment, showing where you would heat.

(b) What precautions would you take before you stopped heating?

6. You are asked to investigate the effect of salt on the melting point of ice cubes.

   Describe the steps that you would take to carry out this investigation using a **filter funnel**, a **measuring cylinder** and a **stop-clock**.

7. Magnesium reacts with sulphuric acid to produce hydrogen.
   Adding copper sulphate solution is thought to speed up the reaction.

   Describe how you would investigate the effect of adding copper sulphate solution on the rate of the reaction between magnesium and sulphuric acid.

8. Heating a mixture of solid ammonium sulphate and sodium hydroxide pellets produces ammonia gas. Ammonia reacts with iron oxide.

   Draw a diagram to show the apparatus that you would set up to make ammonia gas and to pass it over hot iron oxide.

   On your diagram label the apparatus and chemicals used.

9. A class designed the following apparatus to compare the amount of sulphur dioxide released from samples of different solid fuels. The sulphur dioxide changed the orange sodium dichromate solution to a green colour.

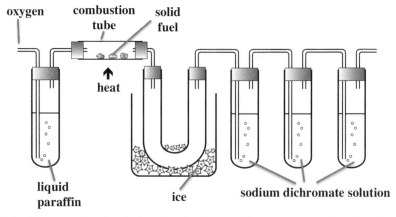

(a) Suggest why the design involved **more than one** test tube of sodium dichromate solution.

(b) Suggest why the oxygen is bubbled through liquid paraffin before entering the combustion tube.

10. Acid rain attacks limestone in buildings. Carbon dioxide gas is produced. It is suggested that painting the limestone would help to resist the attack of acid rain. Two paints are to be tested to compare their ability to protect limestone. Part of the test involves measuring the volume of carbon dioxide produced in any reaction.

    (a) Draw a labelled diagram of the experimental arrangement that could be used for this test.

    (b) State **three** factors that must be kept the same to make the test fair.

11. You are given different compounds and asked to follow the instructions on the workcard to find which of them dissolves fastest in warm water.

    ### Workcard

    1. Pour water into beaker.
    2. Add compound being tested and start stopclock.
    3. Stir.
    4. When the compound has completely dissolved, stop the clock.

    State **three** factors that must be kept the same to ensure a fair experiment.

12. The following experiments were set up to investigate the rate of reaction of four metal powders with dilute hydrochloric acid.

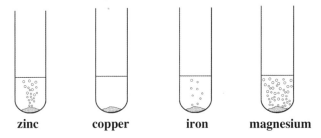

zinc **copper** **iron** **magnesium**

    State **three** factors which must be kept the same for the comparison to be a fair one.

13. The ability of different substances to conduct electricity when dissolved in water was investigated.

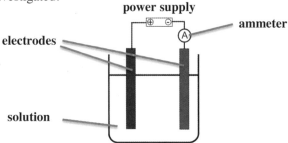

Identify **two** variables that must be kept constant to make the investigation fair.

14. Six experiments were set up to find out which of two tablets, **X** and **Y**, dissolved more quickly in water.

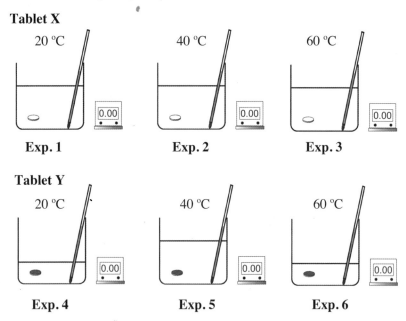

(a) Why would Experiments 2 and 5, taken together, provide the fairest way of comparing how quickly **X** and **Y** dissolved?

(b) The results of the Experiments 1, 2 and 3 can be compared.
    What would this comparison show?